DYNAMITE HILL

OTHER BOOKS BY ROBERT J. ADAMS

*   *   *

THE STUMP FARM

BEYOND THE STUMP FARM

HORSE COP

FISH COP

THE ELEPHANT'S TRUNK

THE SOUTH ROAD

SKUNKS & HOUND DOGS

IN THE SHADOW OF THE ROCKIES

DYNAMITE HILL

To: Bill.

Happy reading

2005

ROBERT J. ADAMS

MEGAMY

THE PUBLISHER:

Megamy Publishing Ltd.
P. O. Box 3507
Spruce Grove, Alberta, Canada T7X 3A7
E-mail: megamy@compusmart.ab.ca

Library and Archives Canada Cataloguing in Publication
Adams, Robert J., 1938–
    Dynamite Hill/Robert J. Adams

ISBN 0-9733728-1-8

    1. Adams, Robert J., 1938– 2. Canadian wit and humor (English) Anecdotes. I. Title.

PS8551.D3224D96 2004   C818'.5402   C2004904007-3

Senior Editor: Kelly Hymanyk
Copy Editor: Natalie King
Design, layout, and production: Kelly Hymanyk
Cover: NEXUS Design
Printing: McCallum Printing Group Inc

DEDICATION

To my grandparents John and Veona Ernst for their role and inspiration in my journey to adulthood. To my granddaughters Megan and Amy for helping me rediscover the magic and excitement of youth.

I am thankful for a lifetime of unforgettable heart warming relationships that have taken me from childhood to my golden years.

CONTENTS

DISCLAIMER

The stories you are about to read are all true. The men, women, and children you will read about are all people from my past. I have taken the liberty of changing the names of many of them to protect their identities. Although I view the past as being very humorous, they may not.

ACKNOWLEDGEMENTS

I would like to thank Mar for her continued support in my writing endeavours. Without her invaluable assistance Dynamite Hill might never have been possible.

Thanks to Larry and Judy for providing much needed assistance in recalling some of the days on the Stump Farm — and their great hospitality on my Calgary runs.

I would like to acknowledge Natalie King's great job of copy-editing. And special thanks to Greg Dussome for his creative cover design.

It seems that I always leave my daughter Kelly for the end. That is because she is number one. Without her there would be no Stump Farm book or Stump Farm series. The Stump Farm, on the South Road just a little south of the town of Edson, would have passed into oblivion, unknown to history, as have so many little farms and lives in the Canadian west. It was Kelly's insight that led to our preserving this little bit of Canadian history. Once again, Kelly, I thank you from the bottom of my heart. You are a gem.

INTRODUCTION

DYNAMITE HILL, Robert J. Adams' newest collection of Stump Farm stories, focuses on his humorous and heartwarming childhood adventures involving his grandparents. As Adams' daughter, I was touched by the bond that was evident between them. After reading these stories, I am happy to reflect on the closeness of my children to their grandparents.

Today often appears to be a time of distance between people, both geographical and emotional distance. Our lives are moving so quickly we don't seem to have time for the simple things in life. My wish for everyone, children and grandparents alike, is that they be able to find happiness in things as simple as a jam sandwich.

Kelly Hymanyk
Megamy Publishing Ltd.

DYNAMITE HILL

NOTHING LIKE
THE SMELL OF BACON

My grandfather was a man of his word. He came from a generation of men where your word and your handshake was as good as — no, it was even better than any contract drawn up by a bank or a lawyer.

I grew up with Grandfather never much more than a stone's throw away. His house was located on the South Road, less than half a mile north of our Stump Farm. My dad and my grandfather were more than just father and son-in-law; they were best friends and had worked together in the bush camps for many years. It was while working in the camps that they met the man who was to sell them the property of their dreams, one hundred and sixty acres of the richest farmland around Edson. In the early 1940s Grandfather and Dad pooled their resources and bought that land, a quarter section south of Edson. Dad got the eighty acres on the south half of the quarter; Grandfather got the eighty acres on the north end, the one with the house on it. They were going to settle down in one place and become farmers.

The land they bought was good farmland, the man had assured them. Why, just under the trees that covered the land was the richest soil in the country, as black as coal. And why wouldn't they believe him? He had given them his word and a handshake to seal the deal.

Most of the land south of Highway 16 and east of the South Road was already broken and producing crops. There was a big farm just south of the highway. The land immediately east of their quarter was broken and being farmed, and the Sliva boys at the end of the South Road had a large dairy farm. Yes, the land Grandfather and Dad had purchased was only a road allowance away from farms, and successful farmers. Their quarter section lacked only two energetic men — and neither my father nor my grandfather was a stranger to hard work, be it in the field or in the bush. Clearing this land was just a minor obstacle that could be easily overcome. All they had to do was break their land, clear it of trees and brush, pull the stumps, pick the rocks, plow the land, and sow the seed.

On the surface and from the South Road, it appeared that the two lumberjacks had picked the ideal place to settle down and do a little farming. After all, just as the man had said, the north half of the quarter, Grandfather's eighty acres, even had a small field that paralleled the South Road. The field was no more than, oh, maybe a hundred feet wide, but it was a place to begin and it could easily pasture a couple of milk cows and a horse or two. Dad didn't have either a cow or a horse at that point, but Grandfather did. And there was an added bonus — the little field was fenced. Yep, that fence ran along the perimeter of the field and appeared to run right back into the bush on the west side of the field. From the South Road, Grandfather's half of the quarter appeared to be completely fenced. Everything was exactly as they were told it was, or so it appeared to be.

An inspection of the fence, just to make sure there were no holes or downed wires, revealed a small gap. They found some wire and a few posts missing on the fence along the south side of Grandfather's eighty acres. It was at a place where the good farming soil seemed to be a little thin. They tried to follow a line back into the trees, which quickly gave way to brush and muskeg, in their search for the wire and posts that would signal an end to the gap. But it was not easy walking back there, and they soon came to the conclusion that the gap in the fence went all the way around Grandfather's eighty acres to a point where the north end of the fence disappeared into the trees. Here, the fence went only a few feet into the trees as well, and then there was a drastic change to the landscape. It was not a change for the better. The lumberjacks-turned-farmers were discovering that all was not what it appeared to be.

They had bought one hundred and sixty acres of what constituted some of the best muskeg to be found in the entire Edson area. Most of their land was black soil all right, but to their dismay it was about the same consistency as soup. It was nothing more than a floating quagmire covered with black spruce, tamarack, and willows. As they found out when they were checking the fence, no one could walk through the area without getting wet. If you were really lucky, and light on your feet, it was only the feet that got wet; but more likely you would find yourself floundering in water up past your knees. More than once in later years I prayed that I would not break through the thin layer of moss and swamp grass that covered the area. Just beneath the surface the black soil — a foul-smelling soupy mess we referred to as "loon shit" — waited to coat everything it touched. The whole area was prone to shaking and vibrating like a bowl of jelly. I myself had stood beside a spruce tree in that muskeg, and by jumping on a root, I was then able to watch every tree in the area jiggle and sway. There was no doubt, farming this land was going to be a challenge.

One would think that just the revelation of what had happened would have been enough to defeat lesser men, but not Dad and Grandfather. Indeed, Grandfather did not appear to look unfavourably on this unfortunate turn of events. It seemed to me that he looked on it as an opportunity. He realized immediately that he was never going to have a farm like the one across the road. But he had bought a farm, and by hook or by crook, a farm he was going to have. And thus, the eighty acres to the north of the Stump Farm became Grandfather's farm.

The small pasture, as intended, was used for his

horses and his cows. He never did fence the back of the pasture. There was a reason that fence never went any farther, for no self-respecting horse or cow would ever wander into that quagmire.

It seemed that Grandfather toiled away day and night. Behind the farmhouse, at the edge of the muskeg, Grandfather built a huge barn which he divided into small pens, and next to the barn he constructed a larger pen. Then he got himself two hogs, an old sow and a boar, which he put into the outdoor pen. One day the old sow was gone from the pen, and we heard the squeals of little pigs coming from the barn. Grandfather had moved the old sow into a pen in the barn, and soon we kids were clambering up the side of the stall to get a look. The old sow was lying on her side, and all along her belly were piglets aplenty, cute little pink guys, eating while the old sow lay there and grunted.

It wasn't long before Grandfather got another sow and put her in with the old boar, then another, and it seemed like it was no time at all before there were hogs of all sizes on Grandfather's eighty acres of muskeg farm. Yes, Grandfather had chosen to raise hogs, and raise hogs he did.

When the piglets were old enough to go outside, Grandfather fenced in a small section of his muskeg, giving the hogs a place to run. Those hogs loved that muskeg. They would spend all day rooting around in it. They dug up the moss and grass that covered the soupy, stinky black soil and created wallows; then, grunting contentedly, they'd almost bury themselves in that stinking black goo. There they'd lie all day; at least, all day until it was time to eat. The only sign of life was the occasional flip of an ear to dislodge a fly or mosquito, and in the summertime there were flies and mosquitoes by the jillions.

Now, Grandfather's hogs loved to eat even more than they loved wallowing in the muskeg, and therein lay a dilemma, for Grandfather did not have land on which he could grow any grain to feed his hogs. Nor did he have the financial resources to purchase as much grain as he needed to feed his rapidly growing herd. From the outset feed was a problem, and in order to be a successful hog farmer, he had to develop other sources. So, being a very resourceful man, he devised a plan. It was a plan with both short- and long-range goals, and one that would grow along with the number of hogs. He would purchase a small amount of grain, but the bulk of the pig feed would come from the good people in Edson, free of charge.

Every day, as regular as clockwork, Grandfather would hitch up his horses — to a wagon in the summer and a sleigh in the winter — and head out for Edson with several large, empty forty-five-gallon barrels. He had an unwritten contract with each restaurant in town to collect and remove the waste food every day. Every day he would return to the farm, with those barrels filled to the brim with the spoils from the day before.

I don't know where he had gotten it, but back at the farm he had a very large cauldron which was set up over a firepit. Into the cauldron he would empty the barrels of kitchen scraps, and to this he would add water and grain. Then he lit a huge fire and boiled the whole concoction. Once Grandfather was satisfied that the mixture was cooked, it was removed in five-gallon pails and poured into troughs. Pigs, covered with the black liquid soil, would be lined up at the troughs, squealing their fool heads off as they waited for their dinner to be served.

For us kids, Grandfather's chosen method of feeding his hogs had its benefits. Whenever Grandfather was running a little late, we were able to get a ride home from school. Grandfather was always happy to oblige his grandchildren or their friends with a ride. The downside was that Grandfather's collectings from the day left much to be desired. To say that his hog feed was a little ripe was an understatement, especially in the summertime, when it was for the most part downright rank. If your nose hadn't been working too good and you didn't happen to smell him coming, you were sure to hear the buzz from the swarm of flies that blackened the sky over his wagon and that he took home with him every day.

I can vividly remember one such day, when Grandfather was returning to his hog farm. On that day he was running late, but he was in a very happy mood. His hog farm was doing well, and Grandfather was doing . . . well, he was doing even better, for I do believe that he had stopped at the "dime store", a term used to describe a beer parlour, to wet his whistle for the drive home. It was a very hot day in early May. There was a slight west wind blowing, and school had long since been let out for the day. We should have hurried home from school and tended to our chores, like good kids, but it was a great day for playing marbles, and that is exactly what we were doing. Mom would not be pleased with us.

A group of us boys were taking our time as we walked home along Highway 16, playing a game of chase with our "boulders", large marbles that were highly prized. One of the boys playing marbles with us was new to Edson, and he had never had the pleasure of experiencing Grandfather's pig feed when it was at its aromatic best. But that was about to change.

I can still see the new kid, all hunched over; he had my boulder in his sights and he was concentrating on his next shot. I had a sick feeling in my stomach as I realized that I was about to lose my boulder. Of course, that was what the game of marbles was all about—win a boulder one day, lose it the next—but man, I hated it when I lost. I, too, was concentrating on his shot, and I was really surprised when his marble shot away from his hand, not even close to my boulder.

"Ohh yyyeeekkkk," he screeched, and his marble shot away, bouncing off the gravel along the edge of the highway before disappearing into the new shoots of grass in the ditch. At the same time, his hands flew up to his face and he gagged. He was covering his face with his hands as he stumbled off the highway, following his marble into the ditch.

I looked up just in time to see Grandfather, his aromatic wagon, and the cloud of flies approach. I had been so busy that I hadn't even seen or heard him coming. I hadn't smelled him either. That was one thing about spending an awful lot of time helping my

Grandfather—it seemed like I had become immune to the smells associated with raising pigs.

"Whoa, horse, whoa-up!" Grandfather sang out as he pulled back on the reins. The horse stopped and the wagon rolled to a halt on the gravel, right opposite the boy in the ditch.

"Arrgh," groaned the boy. He seemed to be fighting for air as he lost his balance and rolled over, his hands still covering his face.

"Are you okay, Boy? Are you hurt?" Grandfather asked, and those of us who knew him could detect a little bit of a grin tickling the corner of his mouth.

"Oooohhh, aaahhhh, ooouuuww," moaned the boy, his only response.

"Would ya like a ride, Boy?" Grandfather asked. The boy immediately shook his head, indicating that he did not want a ride. Then he took one hand from his face and waved frantically for Grandfather to move on.

"C'mon," Grandfather said, half singing the words, "whoever wants a ride better git aboard." We never turned down a ride, especially not a ride with Grandfather. All of us, grandchildren and our friends, gathered up our marbles, stuffed them in our pockets, climbed on the wagon, and sat down. That is, all of us except the new kid, who was still lying in the ditch.

"Are you sure you don't want a ride, Boy? I can't wait forever, you know," Grandfather said. And the boy waved his hand harder, but the look on Grandfather's face said that he was enjoying this little encounter and that, for the sake of the agonizing boy, he could wait a little longer.

"Ooohhhh," the boy moaned again. "The smell! I can't stand the smell."

"Oh, the smell," Grandfather said, and he laughed. "Well, you take a good whiff of this, Boy. This is what your bacon smells like before you eat it."

The boy stopped his moaning and groaning. He dropped his hands from his face and just stared at Grandfather. The look in his eyes said it all. He'd never eat bacon again.

"Giddy-up!" Grandfather called to his horse, and he started to sing. Yes, singing was a sure sign that Grandfather had stopped at the dime store, while his cargo ripened in the hot sun. "And under her belly we saw the blue sky . . ." he warbled as the wagon rolled along down Highway 16.

SQUIRREL TROUBLES

"Come here, Boy, and let me have a look," Grandfather said.

I could tell that Grandfather was genuinely concerned. Worry lines, like deep furrows on a newly plowed field, creased his old brow as he called and waved his arm, beckoning me to come forward. His eyes darted from one hand to the other. In my left hand I held a .22 rifle, Grandfather's .22, the one with the stock shaved down so that I could get my hand around it. In my right hand — well, you couldn't see my right hand; it was completely engulfed in a white rag, a huge bandage. Reluctantly, I took a small step towards him, then paused and held up my right hand.

"C'mon, Boy, step over here so I can see it," he said. "You know my old eyes aren't as good as they used to be. Now, c'mon and tell me what happened."

"It . . . I-I-I . . ." I stammered, but the words I needed were eluding me. No, I was just having a tough time trying to figure out how I was going to explain to Grandfather why I had that huge bandage on my hand.

"Well, Boy," he said, "are you gonna tell me what happened, or am I gonna hafta guess?" The furrows on the old brow had eased, and a slight smile appeared.

"It-it's all your fault, Grandfather, and th-this stupid gun of yours!" I suddenly blurted out without even thinking. Why would I say such a thing? After all, it wasn't Grandfather's fault. It wasn't even the gun's fault. It was my fault that my hand was in a bandage.

"What? Me, Boy? Me and my gun's fault!" Grandfather exclaimed. My sudden outburst wiped the smile right off his face, and it was quickly replaced with a look of shock and surprise. "You didn't go and shoot yourself in the hand, now, did you, Boy?" His jaw sagged and his mouth hung open, and he stared in disbelief at my bandaged hand.

"It-it's like this, Grandfather," I said, and my mind raced as I recalled the events of a few hours earlier when there was nothing in either of my hands. No .22. No bandage. Nothing. I had been one happy little fellow then.

*   *   *

I had got out of school early, at lunchtime. Although it was a cool winter's day, I ran all the way from the red brick schoolhouse to Grandfather's place.

"I need your gun, Grandfather!" I hollered as I raced through his front door. Grandfather was sitting at the kitchen table, eating his lunch. I could tell by the look on his face that he was surprised to see me.

"How come you're not in school, Boy?" Grandfather asked.

"I got out early today," I replied, "and now I'm gonna go and check my trapline before it gets dark."

"What about your chores?" Grandfather asked. "Who's gonna do them?"

"Me," I said. Then I chuckled. "You know, I can always do my chores in the dark, Grandfather, but I can't check my traps in the dark. Mom won't let me."

"Well, I don't know, Boy. You know when I'm butcherin', that gun stays here, and I'm butcherin' a couple of pigs tomorrow so I'm gonna need that gun," Grandfather said.

"Please, Grandfather!" I begged. "Please? I'll bring it back tonight, before I do my chores. I'll even bring it back before I eat. Please!"

"Well, as long as you promise to bring it back, Boy," Grandfather said, "because I don't want to have to go looking for that gun when I'm ready to butcher them pigs."

"I'll bring it back as soon as I've finished checking my traps," I said. I didn't wait for Grandfather to get up; I looked behind the door, where he usually kept his .22. Like most people on the farm, he liked to have his gun where it was right handy, just in case it was needed in a hurry. The gun was there, just like I knew it would be. There was no time to waste. I grabbed that sleek little .22, turned, and raced out the door. Once more I ran down the South Road towards home and my trapline.

25

Mom must have seen me running down the driveway, for she met me at the door.

"Bobby, what on earth is wrong? Why are you home from school so early?" she asked.

Mom was more surprised to see me than Grandfather was. She wasn't nearly as easy to convince that I had gotten out of school early, but some fancy talking on my part convinced her that I wasn't playing hooky. Anyway, who would be stupid enough to come home if they were playing hooky? As quick as I could, I exchanged my lunch pail for my squirrel-hunting knapsack and hustled my butt out the door.

I checked the traps in the stand of spruce trees behind the barn, but they were both empty. From there I walked south, following my trail through the deep snow, across the field that Dad had cleared of trees. The trees were long gone, but the stumps were still there. My trail wound its way around the stumps and I continued on, through a stand of willows and small spruce.

I just knew that this was going to be one of those lucky days. I could feel it in my bones. It was the kind of day that a person would dream about—everything was going to be great. In fact, if I hadn't been so concerned about scaring my prey, I could easily have broken into a song, or at least whistled a tune. But the music could wait until I was returning Grandfather's .22.

At the next stand of spruce trees, my "feelings" were confirmed. The scattered chewings from the spruce cones at the site of the first trap I looked at told me I had been successful. Sure enough, there was a red squirrel in the trap.

With all the confidence in the world, I shifted Grandfather's .22 to my left hand and reached down to pick up the squirrel and the trap with my free hand. Well, that's what I normally did, but for some reason, this time I stuck out my index finger and gave the squirrel a little nudge. I thought he was dead, he was lying there so quiet and still. But he wasn't dead — he was very much alive. As soon as the tip of my finger touched his little body, that stupid squirrel moved, and he just about scared the life right out of me. I recoiled like a sprung spring, and I bounced about a foot off the ground. Even before I hit the ground, my feet were backpedalling as fast as they could go. I dropped that squirrel and jerked my hand away.

Now, I can tell you, I was fast but I was not fast enough. In a flash that little squirrel had whipped his head around, and I quickly found out that he was much faster than me. It seemed like slow motion as he opened his mouth wide — well, as wide as a squirrel can open its mouth — and he bared his little teeth, all stained orange from chewing on spruce and pine cones. Then, to my horror, he aimed those teeth right at my finger, the finger I had touched him with. Those little jaws of his snapped shut and his stained teeth disappeared.

About that time, I remembered that my trap was on a very short chain, and both the squirrel and I hit the end of it very quickly. The trap, the squirrel, and Bobby Adams all came to a sudden, violent stop. It all happened so fast, I couldn't believe it. In shock, I looked down at that angry little squirrel and I couldn't see his teeth. They had disappeared, all right—they were buried right between the second and third knuckle of my index finger.

I tried to retrieve my hand, but that darned squirrel had a real toothlock on my finger and he wasn't about to let go. I could only pull my hand so far, and then it stopped. Yes, my hand was attached to the finger that was being held fast by the squirrel, who was being held by the trap, that was hooked onto the chain, that was fastened to the tree. It was strange, but my finger didn't hurt. However, instinct told me to get my finger back, away from those sharp teeth. Every time I tried to pull my hand away, I could hear the chain. It rattled when I moved my finger, it rattled when the squirrel moved, and it rattled when the trap left the ground.

"Whoa! Let go, you little devil!" I suddenly screamed as a flood of tears filled my eyes. "Let go of my finger before I—"

I never finished my threat, for I could suddenly feel the pain from those little chompers shooting through my finger, through my hand, and up my arm. Instantly, blood from my finger was squirting out in all directions, staining the snow a bright red. But that little squirrel was not distracted. His teeth were firmly embedded in my finger and they were not letting go.

Now, I don't know exactly when it happened, but at some point during that confrontation with the squirrel, Grandfather's .22 and I had parted company. Without even realizing it, I was beating on that squirrel with my left hand. I swatted it, I swiped at it, and I pounded on that stupid squirrel. But that little squirrel was one tough customer — he just bit harder and kicked like a maniac every time I touched him. All the while, those little claws were raking my fingers and my hand. There was no way that little devil was letting go of his prize. The more I beat on him, the more he chewed and clawed.

When I realized that swatting, hitting and pounding wasn't going to help me rid myself of that bloody squirrel, I looked around for Grandfather's .22. Yes, Grandfather's .22 — the sleek, modified version that had the stock shaved down and varnished, the one that fit me to a T — was exactly what I needed to get the squirrel off my finger. I spotted the stock sticking out of the snow and reached for it. But I, like the squirrel, was being held by the chain on the trap, and the chain was too short. My trap and the squirrel and my finger held me back. The gun was just out of my reach. With my free hand I was able to break a dead branch off the spruce tree. I stretched as far as I could, and after some pretty fancy words and a lot of tears, blood, sweat, and pain I was finally able to snag the strap of the .22. I dragged it through the snow to where I could pick it up with my left hand. I had a devil of a time pulling back the hammer. Finally, I held the gun between my knees and cocked the hammer.

"Now it's payback time!" I cursed at that squirrel, and I raised the .22 and pointed it in the direction of the squirrel, who was still firmly attached to my finger. Holding the gun in my left hand, I was gonna shoot that squirrel right off my finger. Through my teary eyes, however, I noticed that Grandfather's stupid gun wouldn't co-operate. Oh, with my left hand I could hold the gun up all right, and I could aim it pretty straight, but when I looked down the barrel, the end of it was about two inches past the squirrel that was still chawing down on my finger. Just my dumb luck—the chain on the trap was too short, and now the barrel on the gun was too darned long! No matter what I tried, the ruddy barrel was just beyond that squirrel's head.

In desperation I dropped the gun and fell to the ground. I tried to put my foot on the spring of the trap to release the squirrel, but I couldn't get my foot to work properly. Finally, risking my good hand, I reached into that furry fury and was able to ease the tension off the spring. The trap opened. The squirrel was free. But that little devil still didn't let go of my finger; he continued to chew away.

I cursed and swung my hand, my finger, and that squirrel at a big spruce tree. That did it. I dislodged him. The squirrel hit the ground, and before I could move, he scrambled down a hole and hid in his den like a coward.

Still in pain, I pulled Grandfather's .22 out of the snow and then I raced for home.

"My Lord, Bobby, what have you done now?" Mom exclaimed, and almost fainted when I barged through the door. By now I was really covered in blood.

"My finger!" I howled. "My finger's gone!"

"Oh no! What have you done to yourself?" she wailed, charging across the room to inspect my hand.

"I was attacked!" I howled. I raised my chewed-up

right hand for her to see, as a new flood of tears streamed down my face.

"Get over here to the wash basin, and let me clean you up," she said. While Mom washed my chewed-up finger, I told her the whole story. She was not impressed.

"I hafta take Grandfather's .22 back," I howled. "He said I hafta take it back as soon as I'm finished with it. And I'm finished with that stupid gun!"

"You can take it back after I've taken care of that hand," she snorted.

Mom was concerned, but she was not too happy either. She washed my hand in the basin, with ice-cold water. Blood continued to flow from the open wounds on my finger. Mom heated up some milk and mustard. She got an old white sheet and ripped it into little strips and soaked them in the mixture. Then, with a firm look in her eye, she came at me.

"What's that?" I asked, pulling back.

"It's a mustard poultice," she replied. "You could end up with an infection or blood poisoning from that wild animal."

She carefully laid strip after strip of that gunk-soaked cloth on my finger and hand. She tore more strips off the sheet and bandaged my whole hand in the thing. When she finished, my hand looked like a giant rag ball.

*   *   *

"So that's what happened, Grandfather," I said.

31

"I see, Boy," Grandfather said, but he had a questioning look on his face, and he added, "but I don't see how any of that is my fault, or my gun's."

"It is!" I said. My finger was throbbing, and I was storming mad. "It's all your fault and th-that stupid gun's fault. I-if you had sawed off the stupid barrel when you shaved off the stock, then the gun would have been shorter. Then I'd have been able to shoot the squirrel off my finger and . . . and . . ." I stopped in mid-sentence.

Holy cow, I thought to myself. I stood there with my mouth hanging open and looked Grandfather straight in the eye. Now I was really embarrassed.

At that moment I realized how stupid I sounded, and a scene flashed before my eyes. It was Bobby Adams, walking around the Stump Farm; and where his right hand had been, there was a hook.

"I . . . I'd have probably shot my hand off," I said sheepishly.

DAD'S MULLIGAN STEW

Spring had come early in the Edson country, but it was not a warm, friendly spring. It was a cold, wet, miserable spring. The howling west wind lashed through the spruce and pines incessantly; rain fell in sheets, pelting the countryside. The snow had melted, filling the ditches to the brim, and the rains had caused them to overflow. The South Road was a series of little lakes and a sea of mud. Yes, the South Road was at its rubber-boot-eating best.

However, as the old saying goes, every cloud has a silver lining. The early breakup and the miserable weather made it impossible for the men to work in the bush camps north of town. It was a happy family that welcomed Dad home earlier than usual.

As it turned out, Dad's coming home early was a

blessing in disguise, for Mom had not been well. She had been to see the doctor in Edson, but the country doctor had not performed any miracles. Mom had continued to ail, and it was decided that she needed the kind of doctoring that could be found only in the big city. Grandfather and his Model T came to the rescue, and rain or no rain, Grandfather would transport Mom to the big city of Edmonton.

The roar of the motor in Grandfather's Model T as it plowed through the mud on the South Road could be heard above the howling of the wind and the splattering of driving rain on the windows. We all raced to look outside, crowding around the window to watch as Grandfather coaxed his old car down the South Road. There was no fear that he would run into the ditch, because his wheels were well entrenched in the water-filled ruts. Grandfather and his Model T were going wherever the ruts on the South Road took him. We watched as the Model T neared our driveway and stopped in the middle of the South Road. There were no ruts leading into the Stump Farm. We didn't have a car, and since the South Road was a sea of mud, and had been for some time, we had not had any visitors with cars.

Grandfather and his Model T sat on the South Road. Through the rain we watched as he slid over to the passenger's seat and peered out the window. He rolled down the window and took off his cap before he stuck his head out. As the rain beat down on his bald head, he looked towards the back of the car. Then he looked towards the front of the car. Then he stared at the driveway. His Model T was firmly locked in the grip of the ruts on the muddy road. He leaned back in the car, replaced his hat, rolled up the window, and there he sat. For a long time, he didn't move as he contemplated the situation. At last he opened the passenger door and leaned out, way out, over the mud and the water, and he looked towards the wheel at the back of the car. Then he lifted his head and took another long look at our driveway. After carefully scrutinizing the situation, Grandfather closed the door and slid back to the driver's side of the Model T. Once more the engine roared, the rear wheels whined as they spun in the mud and water, and slowly the Model T grudgingly inched back a few feet.

Finally Grandfather slid over to the passenger's side of the car and tentatively stepped out, into the wind, into the rain, and into the mud that was the South Road. Down went his feet, and as each second ticked by, they sank deeper and deeper into the mud. For a minute or so, I thought Grandfather might disappear, but then he stopped. He reached into the back of the Model T and pulled out a shovel. Then he struggled, pulling first one foot out of the mud and taking a short step before pulling the other one out, as he slogged his way to the front of the car. There he stopped and looked longingly at the house; then he started to dig. First he made a trench from the right-hand rut into our driveway. Then he seemed to measure something before he began to dig a second trench from the left-hand rut. Grandfather was as busy as a little beaver rearranging the mud on the South Road. Mounds of mud grew as he dug, hoisted, then shook the dickens out of the shovel to dislodge shovelful after shovelful of the sticky clay that was the South Road. When he had finished, Grandfather had created his own set of ruts so that he could get into our driveway.

His digging completed, Grandfather splashed and slogged his way back to the Model T, threw the shovel into the back, and slid in behind the wheel. Once more the motor roared, the wheels spun like crazy, and the Model T slowly, reluctantly, moved forward. It jumped and jerked as the front tires bit into the newly created ruts. Grudgingly the car left the South Road and moved into our driveway.

Grandfather finally entered the house. He was soaking wet and his boots, covered in mud, looked like giant balls of clay.

"You can thank the Sliva boys that I'm even here," Grandfather said, and he smiled as he doffed his cap. He slapped the cap on his sleeves and pant legs, sending a shower of water throughout the kitchen. Whether they wanted it or not, everyone had their fair share of water by the time Grandfather stopped beating his cap around.

"Is that so?" Dad said.

"It sure is. I didn't even have to steer 'er once till I got to yer driveway," he laughed. "Once I got the wheels in the ruts, that old car just came down the road like she knew where she was goin'. Yessiree, I can tell you, Boy, if those Sliva boys didn't have that army truck to haul milk and make them ruts, nobody would ever git down that road in this weather. Nobody," he repeated, shaking his head and slapping his pant legs again with his cap. "Why, that road is like a lake, a lake of mud!"

"If the roads are that bad, how . . . how are we gonna get through, all . . . all the way to Edmonton?" Mom asked. Mom looked worried.

"Railroad, Girl," Grandfather replied. "We're gonna take the railroad tracks."

"The railroad tracks?" I asked. "Wow!" I wasn't going to Edmonton, but I was sure excited at the thought of Mom and Grandfather's impending adventure.

"Wouldn't it be easier if I just took the train in the first place?" Mom asked.

"Don't you worry, Girl, I got it all figured out," Grandfather replied quickly. "I'm gonna wait at the crossing till a freight train comes through. Then we'll jump the tracks, right behind the last car, and we'll straddle the rails. We'll drive on the ties. I'll bet we can follow that train all the way, right into Edmonton. I figure it'll be better to follow a freight train, because they're slower than the passenger trains."

"I don't know, that worries me," Mom protested. Suddenly she seemed to be a lot sicker than she had been. "Just the thought of driving down them tracks chasing a . . . a freight train scares me. I . . . I don't like it. Do . . . do you think we can make it to Edmonton in one day?"

"I think so, Girl, but if we don't, we can always spend the night in Wildwood. Now, don't you worry none," Grandfather assured her. "I said I got it all figured out. You just leave the drivin' and the worryin' to me."

Wow, I thought. This was my kind of adventure. This wasn't a trip for Mom, this was a trip that I should be taking with Grandfather. Man, I could just see Grandfather and me sitting in that Model T, racing down the railway tracks. I could even feel the constant bumping of the wheels as they hit every tie. It would be even better than when the South Road dried up and was like a washboard. I could just see it now — why, I could even hear Grandfather yell at me as the Model T raced over the railroad trestle where the tracks crossed the McLeod River. 'Hang on, Boy!' he would yell, and laugh.

"C'mon, Girl, I haven't got all day!" It was Grandfather's voice that jarred me back to reality. He was urging Mom to get moving. Grandfather was up to the challenge of driving the railroad behind the freight train, and he was anxious to get going.

Mom wasn't as sure as Grandfather. I could see the worried look in her eyes. She was hesitating.

"C'mon, Girl, that freight train won't wait all day!" Grandfather roared again. "Let's go!"

"Bob, are you sure you'll be okay?" Mom asked. "Maybe I shouldn't go. I can wait till the roads are in better shape."

"We'll be fine, Florence," Dad assured her. Then he chuckled and added, "We'll just live the life of a bachelor until you get back."

"I know, that's what worries me," Mom replied.

Mom didn't appear to be all that convinced that she was doing the right thing. She had never left her kids with anybody before, not even Dad, and she wasn't sure that she wanted to now. It was the first time in my life that I could remember Dad being at home with us kids when Mom wasn't there.

"I made enough soup for a couple of days," Mom said. She was having a difficult time dragging herself away from the door. "And there should be enough bread there for a week."

"We'll be fine, Florence," Dad assured her. "We'll be fine. And when the soup's gone, I'll whip us up something that'll stick to our ribs."

We all said our goodbyes to Mom and Grandfather as they left the house. Then we ran to the window and watched Mom take the long walk out to the car. Mom looked sad. She hesitated, and stood in the rain for the longest time looking back at us. We could all see Grandfather waving his hand, motioning Mom to get in. But Mom was not going to be rushed; in fact, it was still debatable if she would even be going.

Grandfather must have been at his wits' end by the time she finally climbed into the Model T.

We stayed at the window and watched. We could hear the roar of the motor above the pounding rain— Grandfather tore up a number of ruts behind the log house as he turned the Model T around and drove away. Water and mud flew in all directions when the tires dropped into the ruts on the South Road. Then Grandfather raised both hands in the air to show us he no longer had to steer, and the roar of the engine faded as the Model T slowly plowed its way north and out of sight. Suddenly, the log house was very quiet.

The quiet didn't last long. Dad was moving the big kettle of soup from the side of the stove over the firebox. Lunch would soon be served. While the soup was warming up, he picked up his guitar and started to pick and sing.

> Oh, little Joe the Wrangler,
> He'll wrangle never more,
> His days they are muted, they are o'er.
> T'was a year ago, . . .

I doubt that Grandfather's Model T had plowed its way to the end of the muddy South Road before my longing for the train-track adventure with Grandfather was forgotten. Yes, this was going to be the life. Dad was home, and when Dad was home, it was good times on the Stump Farm! When the chores were done, there was always pickin' an' singin', for Dad was a great musician. There was always dancing, fun, and laughter. Everybody always said that he was the life of the party. And of course there was always good food . . . but then, Mom had always been home to cook.

This rainy, miserable day was already looking better as we all sat around the table. Dad played the guitar, and we all sang a few of his favourite old cowboy songs until the soup was hot. Dad and my sisters, Gwen and Judy, were real good singers. They were all musically inclined and could keep a tune. Larry and I sang too, but we sang like a couple of coyotes that had been banished from the pack and left on some long-forgotten hill. We had a little trouble keeping on key, but we sang anyway.

One thing I learned that day — the wind and the rain, wishing Mom good luck, and singing cowboy songs sure did make a person hungry. The soup had barely come to a boil when Dad dug the soup bowls out of the cupboard and sliced some of Mom's home-baked bread. Dad was much more generous when he sliced the bread than we were used to. Mom would have said that each slice looked like half a loaf. He gave everybody a healthy helping of soup and an even healthier slab of bread. We all sat down and polished it off.

"Now, that was pretty good," Dad said, smacking his lips as he took another slab of bread and mopped out his soup bowl. "I think that just tasted like a little more. Would anyone care to join me?" We all handed him our bowls and grabbed for a second slab of bread.

When Mom said she had made enough soup for a couple of days and bread for a week, I don't think she had counted on Dad's slicing and dishing-out tendencies. Before we knew what happened, a couple of days' soup and most of the week's supply of bread disappeared at the first sitting. With luck, maybe the bread would last for another day, or at least for supper. One thing was for certain, eating tomorrow would be a whole new adventure.

All night long the wind howled and the rain pelted the log house. Dad was up bright and early the next morning, and another benefit of having Dad home became evident: He had done all the chores before he called us, and he was already cooking breakfast.

Now, Mom had always cooked porridge for breakfast. My sisters ate only Cream of Wheat, so they got Cream of Wheat. Larry preferred Sunny Boy Cereal, so he got Sunny Boy Cereal. And I, the man of the house when Dad was away, ate something that would "stick to my ribs" — I had rolled oats and brown sugar. Yep, Mom knew that breakfast was an important meal, and she made all three cereals every morning. Dad's breakfast, however, was certainly different.

We quickly found out that Dad, for the most part, was a one-dish-meal cook — we all ate the same thing. Dad made flapjacks, and he was a champion flapjack-maker. I could always get three or four of Mom's flapjacks on my plate, but not Dad's flapjacks. When Dad made flapjacks, each one was the same size as the frying pan and each one covered a plate.

"There's enough here for a threshing crew," Dad said, chuckling as he placed a stack of flapjacks on the table. And he was right — his crew of little threshers sat down and polished them off, every last one of them flapjacks.

"It's a good thing that wasn't a pig I cooked up," Dad said. "Or you kids would've eaten everything, including the squeal."

Dad was a good meal-planner, of sorts. He knew flapjacks would not keep us happy all day; and the aroma from the oven told us that lunch was already being cooked. After breakfast he supervised the washing of the dishes, then we all settled in for another bout of guitar-pickin' an' singin'. We spent most of the morning around the table.

Now, sitting around the table and singing cowboy songs on a rainy, windy morning can be mighty tiring, especially when you're not really a singer. Around noon, I was famished.

"Hey, Dad," I called to him in between songs, "I don't think those flapjacks are stickin' to my ribs the way they were this mornin'."

Dad just grinned, then he put his guitar down. He walked over to the stove and opened the oven. A delicious aroma filled the air. He grabbed a big spoon from the cupboard and lifted a healthy spoonful from the pot. First he smelled it.

"Mmmm-mmmm!" He whistled. "Man, do those beans smell good! Can everybody smell the beans?" he asked.

"Wow, beans! I can smell the beans!" I replied. In fact, we all agreed that we could smell the beans. Baked beans were one of my favourites. Man, I thought, Mom had made a huge pot of soup, but that was nothing compared to the pot of beans that Dad made.

"Well, what do you think? Do they smell good?" Dad asked.

"You bet! They really smell good," I agreed. Right then I was as hungry as a horse, and I think anything would have smelled good.

Then he blew on the heaping spoonful of beans and carefully nibbled a few from the spoon. From the way he smacked his lips I knew that they tasted good too. We all grabbed a plate and lined up at the stove and waited while Dad gave each of us a hefty helping of homemade beans. To the heap of beans he added another slab of homemade bread. Once more, we all sat around the table gorging ourselves, this time on beans and bread.

As I gobbled down a bellyful of beans, I knew for sure I was gonna enjoy having Dad around to do the cooking. And I got to thinking about going to school on Monday. Dad's cooking was certainly different from Mom's, and I just had this feeling that there would be something special in my lunch pail. No more peanut-butter-and-jam sandwiches, I chuckled to myself.

As soon as we were full of beans and bread and the dishes were done, the guitar came out again.

The afternoon session of pickin' an' singin' was moving right along with a rousing rendition of "The Strawberry Roan". As the song went, Harry H. Knight had just

> . . . uncoiled his rope, like the whip of a snake,
> Old Strawberry ducked, just a second too late . . .

Suddenly the music slowed, and the guitar-picker lifted his nose and tested the air. The hint of a new odour was drifting through the room. Dad's beans were working, and judging by the odour, they were working real well.

> He got his own saddle and he screwed it on tight.
> Old Strawberry stood there just a-shakin' with fright.

Just about the time old Strawberry was supposed to

wake with a start, a terrible noise erupted around the table. This time the guitar-picker didn't just slow down—he stopped pickin' an' singin'.

Outside the log house, Mother Nature had brewed up a real storm. The wind raged and blew while the rain pelted down in sheets. Inside the house Dad's beans were brewing up a storm of their own. And the fury that blew around the table was enough to challenge the fury of Mother Nature herself. For as long as I could remember, nothing had ever occurred that would hinder a good bout of pickin' an' singin'. But Dad's beans did. Yes, the wind in the bean put a strain on the pickin' an' singin'. One by one, the little stinkers, I mean singers, retreated to a different corner of the room, as far away from anybody else as possible. Dad's beans ruled supreme.

There was no need to prepare something different for supper, as the bean pot still contained a healthy swack of beans. It did not appear that Dad was going to waste a lot of time cooking. Mom thought that she had made enough soup and bread to last a while, but it was evident that Dad had prepared enough beans to last a week. It meant that there was more time left for pickin' an' singin'. The beans were not as welcome for supper as they had been for lunch, but there was no grumbling. "I'm sure glad Dad's home with us and doing the cooking," Larry mentioned that night when we went to bed.

"Yeah, me too," I said.

"You know, Rob, one of the kids in my class doesn't have a mother. He says him and his dad are batching, and his dad makes him bacon-and-egg sandwiches for lunch every day," Larry said.

"No kidding! Boy, is he ever lucky," I said.

"Do you think Dad will make us bacon-and-egg sandwiches?" Larry asked.

"Sure, I'll betcha he does," I replied. "Remember, he said we were going to live the life of a bachelor while Mom was gone."

"I hope so," Larry said.

"You know, come to think of it, I know some kids who get real strange stuff in their lunch pails. There's this one kid who gets goat meat in his sandwiches. He says his dad says that beef is too expensive, and they eat goats all the time. I'm glad we don't have any goats," I said.

"Me too," Larry agreed. "I don't like goats. You know, Rob, there's a girl in my class who only gets a molasses sandwich for her lunch."

"And there's another kid in my room who has this white stuff in her sandwich. She won't tell us what it is, but I think it's lard, because she has a real hard time swallowing it."

"Yeah, lard sticks to the roof of your mouth when you eat it," Larry said. "Do you think Dad will make us bacon-and-egg sandwiches for school?"

"I betcha he will," I replied quickly. "You know, I never had a bacon-and-egg sandwich. I betcha they're a lot better than peanut-butter-and-jam sandwiches."

That night, I went to sleep and I dreamed of bacon-and-egg sandwiches.

Monday morning the wind was still blowing, and

the rain was beating down relentlessly. It was a school morning, and Dad had us up with the birds. Dad had whipped up a batch of flapjacks again, and they would have to stick to our ribs until lunchtime.

We had barely finished breakfast when Ted Sliva and his old army truck stopped at our gate. Ted was the milkman, and he also ran the unofficial school bus on the South Road; every morning, like clockwork, he stopped and picked up all the kids along the road. We all pulled on raincoats and rubber boots, then headed out into the wind and the rain. We sloshed through the mud, being careful to avoid the ruts Grandfather had dug — the ruts were full of water, water that was much deeper than our rubber boots. We piled onto the back of the truck. We sat, with the milk cans and other kids, in the rain and the wind. Slowly, the old army truck plowed through the water and mud, following the ruts all the way to the highway.

I sat in class all morning dreaming of the special lunch Dad had made. I just knew it would be bacon-and-egg sandwiches. When the bell sounded for lunch, I was the first out of my seat. I dashed into the cloakroom and grabbed my lunch pail and raced back to my desk. This was the moment I had been waiting for. The moment to savour. A moment to remember. I tore into the lunch pail and ripped the wax paper off the sandwich. I closed my eyes and sank my teeth into my bacon-and-egg sandwich. However, it tasted suspiciously like peanut butter and jam. For a moment, I thought I would gag, but then I remembered the pot of beans and I gladly ate the peanut-butter-and-jam sandwich, for it could very easily have been a bean sandwich.

Monday was normally baking day on the Stump Farm, which was fortunate because Mom's bread was all gone. Now it was Dad's turn to bake, and he did, but he did not bake bread as we were used to; instead, he substituted one of his favourites. On Monday night we had fresh bannock and beans. On Tuesday we had day-old bannock and beans for supper. And for the rest of the week we had stale bannock and beans for supper. For lunch it was peanut-butter-and-jam sandwiches — made with bannock of course — and for breakfast the old standby, a huge plate-sized pancake.

By the time Friday rolled around, I had concluded that the life of a bachelor was not as glamorous as I had imagined. Oh, it was great to get up in the morning and find that the cows had been milked, the hogs were slopped, and the chickens had been fed. There was a fresh pail of water by the wash basin, and the woodbox was filled to the brim. But the house had not been the same without Mom. The inside of the house hadn't changed, but yet it was different. It was the same stove as always, but there was something about the top; the top never seemed to have the polished or the clean look that only Mom could put on it. And the table — well, it just didn't seem like all the crumbs ever got wiped off it. Even the dishpan was different: there were always some dirty dishes in it. And there were always chips of wood and pieces of bark scattered on the linoleum around the woodbox. Yes, in one short week our home had begun to look like a bachelor's shack. To top it all off, the huge flapjack for breakfast, peanut-butter-and-jam sandwiches for lunch, and the ever-present pot of beans for supper were wearing a little thin. I was even beginning to wonder if Larry's classmate got tired of bacon-and-egg sandwiches every day.

But Friday evening there were some changes in the log house. Oh, we still got a few beans and bannock to work on, but Dad did have a surprise for supper. He had walked into Edson and bought half a roll of bologna.

"Hot diggity dog!" I squealed with delight. I was sure happy with the meat, and also with the fact that the end of the beans was finally in sight. We all watched as Dad cut off huge slices of bologna — "round steaks" he called them — and then he fried them up, one for each of us. It just so happened that I really liked bologna, and fried bologna was the best bologna of all.

On the back of the cookstove was a tub that was almost half full. It didn't belong on the stove, not on a Friday anyway. There were only two days when water was heated in a tub on the stove: on Mondays, wash days, and on Saturdays, bath days. Obviously Dad had another surprise up his sleeve, and as soon as the dishes were done after supper, he put the tub in the middle of the kitchen floor. Bath day had been moved up to Friday night, so that we would be sparkling clean for Mom. One by one — starting with Judy, the smallest member of the family, and ending up with Dad, the largest — we all plunked ourselves into the tub and washed away a week of dirt and batching.

On Saturday morning I was really excited, because it was the day that Mom was coming home. Dad had got us up with the birds, but this time it was so that we could prepare a real meal for Mom. He was still the chief cook, but today we were all going to help in the kitchen. There would be fresh home-baked bread. And there would be one of Dad's very special mulligan stews. We all got a job peeling and cutting up spuds, and carrots, and turnips, and onions, and anything else that wasn't nailed down. There were even a few beans left that we dumped into the pot. Boy, we all knew that Mom was really going to be surprised when she saw the stew, for Dad was renowned for his mulligan stew.

While the bread was baking and the stew was stewing, we all walked outside and patiently waited for Mom to arrive. The wind had finally died down to a light breeze, although threatening, heavy, black clouds rolled across the skies. The rain had stopped, at least for now; however, the South Road was still a sea of mud.

Outside, the air was fresh and crisp and there were new aromas on the Stump Farm. The smell of fresh homemade bread baking in the oven and the tantalizing aroma of Dad's mulligan stew simmering on the stove were overwhelming, and they were making me deliriously hungry. I strained my ears, listening for the sound of Grandfather's Model T. My stomach growled impatiently just thinking of the feast to come.

We had been outside for a while when another smell drifted out from the kitchen. It took us a minute to realize what was happening. We had been so intent on waiting, watching, and listening that we forgot to tend the meal. Someone should have stayed inside with the bread. Now, I can tell you, when you're hungry as a wolf for fresh bread, there is nothing worse than the smell of freshly burned bread. And that is exactly what was happening to our home-baked bread—it was burning. We all raced into the kitchen in time to see the cloud of black smoke pouring from the oven. Dad quickly pulled the bread tins and their burnt offerings out of the oven; then he checked his mulligan stew. We all breathed a sigh of relief when he declared that the stew was saved.

Finally we heard it, the roar of an engine, and we all raced to the edge of the road. There we stood on the grass and watched as Grandfather's old Model T slowly laboured through the ruts on the South Road. As the Model T neared our turnoff, Grandfather threw his hands into the air. There was still no need to steer—the wheels stayed in the ruts as the car churned forward. Grandfather stopped just short of our driveway. I could see him craning his neck. Two tracks filled to the brim with water showed that his hand-dug ruts were still there.

Suddenly the motor roared, and the Model T inched forward. Grit and determination showed on Grandfather's face. His eyes were wide open. His tongue stuck out the side of his mouth through his tightly pursed lips. He cranked the steering wheel to the right and held it there with all his might. Grudgingly the tires entered his man-made ruts. The Model T jumped and bounced and finally turned into our driveway. We all cheered.

"Boy, Grandfather is sure a good driver, isn't he, Dad?" I warbled, proud and happy. Dad just chuckled.

"He does okay," he replied.

"C'mon, Boy!" Grandfather yelled when he stopped the car. "Give your mother a hand here. She doesn't feel good and she's pretty weak."

"It's nothing that a good home-cooked meal won't cure," Mom replied. A faint smile crossed her lips. Mom had been gone only a week, but she did look frail. She was pale and weak. I thought she was supposed to get better in Edmonton, but she looked sicker than when she had left, a week earlier.

"Are you okay, Florence?" Dad asked as he helped her from the car. "Are you hungry?"

"I'm okay. But after eating that hospital food, I'm starved," Mom replied.

"Did you drive on the railroad tracks?" I asked Grandfather.

"I sure did, Boy," Grandfather replied. "Why, I even had to get out of my car and tell that old engineer to get that train moving or I'd be forced to drive right over the top of him."

"Wow! Boy, I'd sure like to drive down the railroad tracks," I said. Grandfather had a way of making any experience sound so exciting.

"Well, you can take my place the next time I have to go," Mom replied. "That ride just about shook the insides right out of me. I'm so glad to be home, I don't care if I never see another railroad track, another doctor, or the inside of another car!"

"C'mon, Boy! Give your mother a hand," Grandfather yelled again. "Get her into the house so she can lay down."

"Oh, it just feels so good to be home, I feel better already," Mom said. "And I could use a rest, but I think I'd like something to eat first, before I lie down."

"Dad made you a mulligan stew," someone said.

"Oh, a mulligan stew!" Mom said, and for a second she got a funny look on her face as if she were trying to recall something. Then she added with a smile. "Yes, a bowl of hot stew would be nice."

We arrived at the door, but Mom hesitated when it was opened. Suddenly there was a look of concern on her face, and she lifted her head and took a deep breath. I took a deep breath too, and the delicious aroma of Dad's mulligan stew tickled my nostrils. Ah yes, I thought, Mom's picked up on the stew. Will she ever be surprised when she sees what we've added, just for her!

"It smells like something's burning," Mom said, completely ignoring the stew.

"We made you some fresh, home-baked bread too, Mom. We made it just for you," I said.

"Yeah, but we forgot it in the oven and it got a little overdone," one of my sisters said.

"Yeah, but you can still eat it," I added. "All you gotta do is trim off the black part."

"It's all black parts," my other sister added.

"Thank you," Mom replied, and her voice sounded weaker than before.

With the help of her family, Mom stepped through the door and into the kitchen. There she stopped for a second time, and she looked around her kitchen. Her eyes roamed over the room. They stopped at the table, as if she was counting every crumb that had not been wiped away. They stopped at the dishpan that was stacked with dirty dishes. Next came the floor and the woodbox, with the chips and bark strewn around. Mom was so happy to be home, I thought I saw a big old tear welling up in the corner of her eye.

"I think I'll have that bowl of stew now and go to bed for a while," she said. "For some reason, I suddenly feel very tired . . . and old."

"You sit down, Florence," Dad said. "I'll get you some stew."

"I'm not helpless. I can serve myself," Mom said. Mom wasn't used to anyone else serving her, especially not in her own kitchen. She slowly shuffled over to the cookstove and there she stopped once more.

"I hope you like it, Florence," Dad said.

"Why wouldn't I like it?" Mom asked. "I'm dying for a good home-cooked meal, and you know how much I like stew. Mmmm, it does smell good."

Mom teetered over the stove and picked up the lid. She closed her eyes and took a deep breath, enjoying the aroma. Then she looked inside. If I thought Mom looked pale before, that was nothing compared to how she looked when she peered into the stewpot. She gasped and held her breath. Whatever her mind had been searching for suddenly came back, and she turned as white as a ghost. For a minute I thought she was going to faint, or she was going to be sick.

"Oh my Lord, Bob!" she gasped. One hand flew up

and covered her mouth, the other clutched at her stomach. "What have you put in the stew?"

"I put in everything. Everything we had left," Dad said.

"What is that?" Mom moaned, pointing into the pot.

"I just added some meat, but I wasn't sure how much I should put in," Dad said apologetically. "I hope there's enough."

"Enough. . . . None would have been too much," Mom said as she dropped the lid back on the pot. She turned and staggered back to her chair. But she didn't sit down. She leaned heavily on the table and stared out the window. Finally she turned back to face us, the stove, and the kettle of stew.

"Would you like some stew now, Florence?" Dad asked. "I'll get you some?"

"No thank you!" Mom snorted. "Now I just want to go to bed." Then she turned and walked into her bedroom. "Hopefully this nightmare will be gone when I wake up," she muttered.

"What's wrong with your mulligan stew?" I asked Dad.

"I don't know," he replied. "It looks good to me." Poor Dad, he looked like he had just been kicked in the head.

I hastened to the kitchen stove, grabbed a dishtowel off the rack, and hoisted the lid off the huge kettle, exposing Dad's mulligan stew. Steam exploded and filled the air with the tantalizing aroma. I couldn't understand why Mom had decided to go to bed without eating. The aroma alone would make a person ask for seconds. The kitchen, the living room, and for that matter the entire house had taken on the aroma of Dad's mulligan stew. It made my mouth water. I closed my eyes and took in a deep breath, savouring the moment. Now, I must say, with a great deal of pride, that Dad's mulligan stews were renowned. They often included unexpected ingredients, because he used whatever was left in the kitchen. Dad took great pleasure in serving mouth-watering stews using only whatever foodstuff was available. This mulligan stew was no exception.

I looked down, down, into the bubbling kettle. Man, but I could almost taste the potatoes, carrots, turnips, and onions. And sitting up high, right on the top of the stew, was a huge piece of meat, the end of the big bologna roll. It protruded majestically above the vegetables and the beans like . . . like a big round-topped hill, or even a mountain. From the peak, there were little gullies running down the slopes. Some of the gullies were man-made , some had been formed during the cooking process. Oh yes, that mountain of meat stuck up a good inch or two above the vegetables and the beans, and yes, it was cooked to perfection. I raced back to the table and grabbed my plate.

"It sure looks good to me, Dad!" I said. I could hear Mom, in the bedroom, groan like she was going to die. As I got an extra-big helping off the end of the roll of bologna that was floating on the top of Dad's mulligan stew, I felt bad that Mom was missing out. This was, after all, the best meal we'd had all week.

DYNAMITE HILL

"Bobby, what do you think you're going to do with that thing?" Mom asked.

I couldn't quite tell by the look in her eyes whether Mom was unimpressed with the ingenuity of my latest creation, or whether she was questioning my sanity. My handiwork was certainly not an object of her affection.

"What?" I asked, as innocent as I could be. Then I proudly looked down at my creation.

"That . . . that contraption. That piece of junk. What on earth is it supposed to be?" Mom asked.

"Oh, this," I replied happily, as I caressed it with my eyes. "This is my toboggan, Mom, a-and I made it, all by myself, with my own two hands. And it didn't cost me nothing, Mom."

Mom and I both stood there and looked at the tattered length of rubberoid roofing that I had pulled out of the garbage dump behind the old outhouse. To get the little curl at the front of my toboggan, I had punched six holes in the roofing—two at the front corners, and then four more, two on each side about two feet back and only an inch apart. I took a couple of pieces of binder twine that had been hanging on the wall in the barn and threaded them through the holes. I tied a willow stick across the front of my toboggan, and carefully rolled up the front and, keeping the curl, I tied the first willow to another willow, which I tied into the remaining four holes. Finally, I tied several more pieces of binder twine together to make a rope to drag the toboggan. It hadn't taken much, and my toboggan was finished. It was perfect. Well, it was as perfect as a tattered piece of rubberoid roofing could be. Now my toboggan and I were ready for action.

"Well, that's very nice," Mom said, and smiled as she took a closer look at my toboggan. "But where are you going to use a toboggan? There isn't a decent hill to toboggan on anywhere near the farm."

"I know that, Mom. I'm gonna use it on Dynamite Hill!" I stated enthusiastically.

"Dynamite Hill?" Mom repeated the name, looking a little puzzled. "I don't know where this Dynamite Hill is. I don't think I've even heard of it."

"Sure you know, Mom. It's right by the hospital. We walk past it every day on our way home from school."

"What! You don't mean that cutbank, that . . . that cliff across from the nuns' residence by the hospital, do you?" Mom said. Uh-oh, I thought, now there's fire in Mom's eyes.

"Yeah, that's it, Mom, that's Dynamite Hill," I babbled excitedly. "See, I told you that you knew where it was." I stood there and beamed happily.

"Oh no you don't, Bobby!" Mom said in a firm voice, and she reached for the binder twine. "You're not going to ride that thing off of any cliff."

"But Mom, why not?" I protested. "It's safe! And — and all the kids are doing it, and most of them don't even have toboggans. All they use are cardboard boxes or just pieces of cardboard."

"I don't care what they're using," Mom stated emphatically. "You'll break your neck if you go flying down that hill."

"Aw, Mom, please?" I pleaded. "I won't get hurt. I promise." Mom looked at me for a long minute before responding.

"Isn't there a creek at the bottom of that hill?" Mom asked.

"Well, yeah, sure, there's a creek there, Mom. It's always been there, and it runs right through the valley, but it's just a teeny weeny little creek and there's no water in it," I replied. I wasn't sure why Mom was interested in the creek. Actually there had been a little water in it, but now it was frozen, solid as a rock. There was no chance of getting wet, if that was her concern.

"That's what I thought."

"But it's way over at the far side of the valley, Mom," I quickly added.

Man, I had been dying to try out my new toboggan ever since I got the idea of how I could build one. When I closed my eyes, I pictured myself careening down that

59

slope. The bottom of my rubberoid-roofing toboggan barely tickled the tops of the bumps as I whizzed down Dynamite Hill. I could even feel the cool breeze whistling in my ears as I flew past my envious schoolmates on my very own toboggan. But the tone in Mom's voice made it obvious that she did not share my enthusiasm. Mom was concerned about Dynamite Hill, and maybe even the creek. I was going to have to do some mighty fancy talking to get her to see my side, to assure her that I knew all about Dynamite Hill and that there was no danger.

But it was Mom who was doing most of the talking.

"That's what I thought, there is a creek at the bottom of the hill. Well then, that settles it," Mom said. There was a firmness to her voice that told me the conversation was over. "You are not to go down that hill on a sleigh, or on a toboggan, or in a cardboard box, or on a piece of cardboard. Do you understand me?"

"But Mom," I pleaded. I ignored the warning in the voice and continued to push my point with some of that fancy talking. "I—" I began, but she cut me off short.

"That's enough, Bobby! The answer is no! Now you have chores to do. Go and do your chores, and I don't want to hear another word about toboggans or Dynamite Hill."

"But Mom—" I started to whine, forgetting all about the fancy talking.

"Chores," Mom said, ending the conversation.

The next day at noon I was feeling pretty low and real sorry for myself. My lunch remained untouched in my lunch pail, in the cloakroom back at the red brick schoolhouse. I shuffled along behind classmates and every other boy in the school as they boisterously raced out of the boys' side of the schoolyard. Most carried or towed an assortment of toboggans, sleighs, cardboard boxes, or pieces of cardboard. I trudged along, alone, behind the horde. I reached the top of Dynamite Hill and there I stood, quietly, sadly, watching my friends scream and yell as they flew down the steep slope of Dynamite Hill.

I watched three of my classmates climb aboard a toboggan that was poised on the brink of Dynamite Hill. They shouted and laughed happily as they prepared for their trip. Then, without any warning, an older boy suddenly raced forward and threw himself on top of the three, and his momentum carried the toboggan forward. In an instant the toboggan, with its human cargo of flailing arms and legs, hit the business part of the hill and careened wildly down the slope. A fine mist of snow sprayed out behind the toboggan, painting a ghostly picture of my departing classmates. They whooped and howled as the toboggan levelled out at the bottom of the hill and raced towards the little creek. It looked as if a collision was inevitable until the older boy on top of the pile rolled off. Suddenly the toboggan flipped and there was an explosion of snow. The air was filled with flying bodies, arms, and legs.

When the snow settled, all was quiet and still.

Then, from the jumble of bodies, arms, and legs came an excited howl.

"Man, was that fun!"

It was the older boy. I watched as he jumped to his

feet and ran back up the hill to hitch another ride.

Then high-pitched laughter cut through the crisp air, as my classmates disentangled themselves. They scrambled to their feet, and towing their toboggan they started for the top of the hill and another run.

I felt tears welling up in my sad eyes as I surveyed Dynamite Hill. I'll bet there wasn't an inch of that hill that didn't have someone flying down it or someone crawling up it, dragging a toboggan, or box, or whatever, back to the top to start anew. I couldn't believe what my mother had done to me. I knew she couldn't have known how much fun she was depriving me of, or else she wouldn't have placed those ridiculous restrictions on me. Grounded me. As I looked with desire over the steep slope, I saw probably every boy in the red brick schoolhouse out on Dynamite Hill. Every boy, that is, except me. Bobby Adams was being a good boy, standing at the top, listening to his mother, while all the other boys were enjoying themselves.

"Hey, Bob!" I heard someone call my name. I looked across the top of the hill to where the voice came from. It was one of my classmates, and he was waving wildly.

"What?" I called back in my miserable little voice.

"C'mon, join me!" he yelled above the din.

"I can't," I growled back. Then, so no one else could hear, I mumbled to myself, "My mother won't let me."

"Sure you can," he replied in an encouraging voice. "Look, I've got me a sheet of tin. I'll bet we can go faster than anyone else. In fact, we'll probably be going so fast that we'll fly right across the creek."

"A sheet of tin!" I howled. Then I gave a little

chuckle and looked skyward. Now, this was indeed an unexpected, pleasant surprise. A gift from above. I very carefully went through the list of things that Mom had told me not to go down Dynamite Hill on, and guess what—a sheet of tin was not one of them. I charged over to my classmate and stared in amazement at his sheet of tin.

"Holy cow, what a great idea. I'll betcha that piece of tin will really fly down Dynamite Hill!" I exclaimed.

"You betcha!" he said, and he laughed. "You should see it go. On the way over here I just gave it a little shove on the road, and it slid forever."

It was just a useless piece of scrap. It looked as if my classmate had been beating on it with a sledgehammer. There were numerous holes in the tin, evidence that at one time nails had been pounded through it to fasten it down. In places, the tin was torn where the nails had resisted the sheet being stripped away from its mooring, and the edges were all tattered and ragged as if someone had just ripped it off a wall, or a roof, or something.

"Where'd you get it from, anyway—the garbage dump?" I asked. I could not help but admire that piece of tin.

"Yeah," he said, and grinned like a Cheshire cat. "I found it last night. I hauled it home and pounded it flat to make a toboggan. C'mon, let's take 'er for a ride."

"You bet!" I yelled. I was thrilled to be the first to accompany my classmate down Dynamite Hill on his piece of tin, and since tin wasn't on Mom's list of no-no's, I forgot all about her.

"Hot dog!" my classmate sang out, giving a hearty laugh as he settled himself on the front of the piece of tin. He reached forward and grabbed the two front corners and pulled them back as far as he could. It wasn't very far, but they curled up enough so that the front of the tin was away from the snow.

"Give me a shove, Bob!" called my classmate. "When she starts to move, jump aboard. But you better be fast, and hang on for your life!"

"Yahoo, look out below!" I yelled, and with that, I leaned forward and put my hands on his shoulders, right beside his neck. I took a step forward and pushed as hard as I could.

My classmate and that piece of tin just shot forward! They took off so fast that I barely had time to think. That tattered old piece of tin was really moving. In desperation, I made a frantic grab and succeeded in latching onto my friend. I had him firmly by the throat as we hit the downslope and picked up speed. I never did get my feet onto the sheet of tin. In no time flat that sheet of tin, with my feet, my legs, and my body bouncing along behind, was screaming down that slope like a drop of water on a hot griddle. I couldn't see a thing for the flying snow, but I could hear the muffled cries of my schoolmate.

"Leggo my throat, you idiot! You're choking me to death!"

Somewhere between the top and the bottom of Dynamite Hill, my school chum managed to shake me off. I lost my grip on his throat. As we parted company, he and his slick piece of tin shot away from me like a bullet. I was following the rapidly departing tin toboggan, rolling and flopping around like a rag doll. I closed my eyes and prayed, for I had no idea which way was up. It was not a glorious feeling. Most of the time I was airborne, and every time I hit the ground it flung me in another direction. My coat filled with snow. The whole world that was Dynamite Hill was spinning crazily. Each time I bounced off the icy surface, I knew Mom had been right—I was going to break my neck.

Finally the world stopped spinning, and I skidded to a stop. Voices of kids having fun began to return. I shook myself, and turned my neck from one side to another. To my relief, it was not broken. I immediately jumped to my feet, as a euphoric sensation swept over me. Now, this was a glorious feeling! It was like nothing I had ever experienced in my life. I was on cloud nine! I unbuttoned my coat and shook out about two pailfuls of snow, then jiggled around to get the snow out from down my neck and out of my long johns. Even my overshoes were full of snow. I laughed as I pulled them off and dumped the snow out.

"Hey, Bob!" I heard someone call my name.

I looked around and spotted my classmate pulling himself out of the creek bed. He looked like he might have come out second-best from his encounter with the far bank of the creek, but he was all right. He was waving at me.

"Hey, c'mon, slowpoke!" I yelled at him over my shoulder, as I started to race up the slope we called Dynamite Hill. "That was fun, hurry it up, time's a wastin'. Let's go again!"

"Look out, Bob!" he yelled back at me, and for a fleeting second I could see the look of terror in his eyes. But it was too late.

I never even heard the freight train coming, let alone saw it. One second, I was there yelling encouraging words to my classmate; the next, my world flipped upside down. Suddenly everything around me was a blur, spinning, twisting, and turning wildly. Then the lights went out and I was swallowed up. I felt a crushing weight on my body as I was being rolled — no, bulldozed down Dynamite Hill. I was being crushed, ground into the hard-packed snow.

Finally the pounding and grinding stopped, and I gasped to draw a breath. In the distance I could hear laughter. The crushing weight was slowly being lifted as, one by one, bodies removed themselves from the pile. Then I could hear the cheering of kids celebrating their latest accomplishment. When the last one rolled off, my classmate pulled the makeshift toboggan off me. It was then I realized that there was more than one sheet of tin on Dynamite Hill. A group of the older kids also had a toboggan made of tin, and they had just ridden the whole thing right over top of me.

I struggled to my feet and promptly fell flat on my face on the packed ice and snow at the bottom of Dynamite Hill.

"Ooww!" I screeched in pain, for it was then, lying flat on my face in the ice and snow, that I became aware of a searing, shooting pain in my right leg.

"It's my leg!" I screamed as I realized it wasn't working so well. "My leg! I broke my leg!" And at that point I remembered Mom's words of warning. Suddenly I forgot about the pain in my leg, for I knew at that moment that Mom was gonna kill me for going down Dynamite Hill. Even a broken leg couldn't override the fear I had at the thought of telling Mom.

"Ah, get up and quit your whining," scoffed one of the older boys. It was he who seemed to be laughing the loudest. He was already tugging at the rope, dragging his sheet of tin back up Dynamite Hill. Yes, he was one of the group who had just ridden over me.

"You broke my leg!" I howled at him.

"It's just a little scratch. You're gonna live, you crybaby!" he said, and he laughed again as he raced after his group.

"Scratch?" I asked. "What scratch?"

Then I rolled over and I saw it, a spot of blood on the snow. Instantly the pain returned to my leg. It started to throb, and sharp pangs shot up through my body. I couldn't believe how the spot of blood was changing to a large red blob that grew larger by the minute.

"My leg!" I howled. "Look at my leg! You've cut off my leg!"

"You better get up and get out of the way before you get run over again, you dummy!" the older boy called back over his shoulder.

"And my pants! Lookit my pants!" I howled. "You've ruined my pants. You've almost cut my pant leg off."

I pointed to the spot at my knee where there should have been cloth, but there was only my bare leg—and

67

it was an ugly, gashed bare leg, and blood was spurting out of the gash, past my pants and onto the snow.

"C'mon, Bob," said my classmate, as he helped me to my feet. "We better get back to school."

With the help of my classmate, I clawed my way back to the top of Dynamite Hill and hobbled back to school. Even though we were supposed to stay outside until the bell rang, the janitor took one look at me and he opened the doors. I hung my coat in the cloakroom and dragged my beat-up, mangled leg into the classroom. There my horrified teacher examined my leg. She confirmed what I already knew. There was a huge gash on my knee, and it appeared to go right around my whole kneecap. My wound was bleeding quite a bit; and because of the blood she wasn't sure, but she thought that she could see the bone. My pant leg had definitely been torn. Luckily the tear was large enough to allow her to see the extent of my injury.

That afternoon, while the rest of my classmates worked, I was allowed to sit there and tend to my injuries. Well, mostly I sat there and bled and cried. I didn't even have to go outside at recess time when the rest of the class was ushered out of the classroom and outside. However, I did have visitors. Recess gave several of the teachers the opportunity to come into the classroom, which must have resembled an examining room. There was little comfort in the fact that they, too, were able to confirm that the knee had been cut and the pants were probably ruined. One after another, the teachers all voiced the same verdict.

Oh, man, I thought, nothing is going to help me now. I began to wish that I could stay in that classroom forever, but I knew that sooner or later I was going to have to go home. Home to the Stump Farm. Home to Mom. Home to the fury that I knew awaited a foolish boy who disobeyed his mother.

Almost dragging my poor leg with the chewed-up knee, it took me a long time to hobble from the red brick schoolhouse to Highway 16. My sister Gwen and my friends had long since walked ahead of me, and I was alone, in my misery, as I limped towards the Stump Farm. I knew that Mom was not going to be happy and that all my chores would still be waiting for me when I got home — that is, if I ever got home.

In the depths of my misery, I didn't even hear the approaching sleigh bells and was startled when I heard a familiar voice.

"Whoa-up," Grandfather called to his horses as he drew up alongside me. A big old smile lit up his face, but it disappeared when he saw my leg. Like a shot, he bailed off the sleigh and raced to my side. He bent over for a better look at my bleeding knee.

"Can — can I get a ride home, Grandfather?" I asked as the tears started to flow down my cheeks. "Mom's gonna kill me."

"Of course you can, Boy. What happened to your leg?" he asked.

Through the sobs and the tears, I told him the whole story. . . .

"And — and Mom is gonna kill me."

"C'mon, Boy," he said, as he lifted me onto the sleigh. Then he sat down beside me, wrapped an arm around me, and pulled me close. "You just snuggle in here and stay warm. I'll take you home to your mother. She might not be very happy with you, but she won't kill you."

I couldn't believe my good luck. Not only was I getting a ride, but Grandfather was taking me home, and I wasn't going to have to face Mom by myself. I started to feel much better as I snuggled in beside him. My leg even started to feel a little better. I listened to the sound of the sleigh bells all the way down the South Road: past Nick-the-Dog-Man's place, where his dogs were barking like crazy; past Grandfather's pig farm; on to the Stump Farm, where he turned off the South Road into our driveway.

Mom must have heard the sleigh bells, and Gwen must have alerted her to my situation, because she was standing at the side of the house waiting for us. She looked awfully mad. Grandfather called to the horses and they broke into a gallop. The horses were going flat out as the sleigh flew right past Mom. In behind the house the horses raced. There, out of sight and a safe distance from Mom, Grandfather turned the sleigh in a tight circle and stopped the team.

"Okay, Boy," Grandfather said, and his voice was loud and clear. "Off you get, now. I brung you home to your mother, just like I promised."

"But . . . but Grandfather, aren't you coming in with me?" I asked as I hobbled off the sleigh.

"I can't help you now, Boy," Grandfather said, and

he slapped the reins on the horses' rumps. The startled horses jumped and took off. I watched helplessly, alone, deserted, as the whole kit and caboodle raced away—and Mom came charging around the corner of the house.

THE BEST DOG IN THE WORLD

Trixie was just a little dog—a white fox terrier with a large black and brown patch that covered his head and face, and no bigger than a minute. On Grandfather's hog farm that little dog walked tall and barked big. He was the self-appointed guardian and protector, and when duty called, Trixie was a pig herder. The best darn pigdog in the world, according to Grandfather.

"I'll tell you, Boy, Trixie's the best dog in the world! No sir, there's not another dog like him," I had often heard Grandfather trumpet proudly.

I wasn't sure that I shared Grandfather's opinion of the little dog. True, I remember one occasion when the little dog really earned his stripes. It was on a night a couple of years back when a bear had got into the pigpen and killed one of Grandfather's prize sows.

When the bear came after Grandfather, it was Trixie who attacked the bear (or should I say the bear's rump), distracting him long enough that Grandfather was able to beat a hasty retreat to the house. But I had more memories of occasions that cast a shadow over Trixie and his title.

I remember one day when Grandfather really needed the best dog in the world. It was just before lunch, and Grandfather was in a hurry. He needed all the help he could get. Grandfather had sold a load of pigs that were ready for market. To finalize the deal, the pigs had to be delivered; but first they had to be loaded onto the back of his truck, and Grandfather was counting on Trixie's help.

"Ma!" Grandfather called to my grandmother as he charged into the house looking for the dog. "Where's Trixie? Have you seen 'im?"

"He's not in my house," Ma replied.

"I can never find that dog when I need him. I'm going to town, but first, I'm gonna load the pigs and have some lunch. I'll be leavin' as soon as I've finished eatin'."

It was Grandfather's way of telling Ma that he wanted his lunch on the table when the truck was loaded. It was also his way of saying that if she wanted to go to town with him, she had better be in the truck when he finished eating. For it was common knowledge that when Grandfather was ready to go, he went. Those that were in the truck went with him; those that were not were left behind. Grandfather waited for no one.

"C'mon, Boy, you can gimme a hand," Grandfather

73

said to me as he rushed out of the house and across the yard.

"Comin'!" I called after him. I had been in the kitchen with Ma, sampling one of her oatmeal-and-date cookies, but here was a chance to help Grandfather, so without any hesitation, I crammed what was left of the cookie into my mouth and raced out the door.

"C'mon, Trixie!" Grandfather called in a loud voice. However, the best dog in the whole world hadn't heard the call; at least, if he did, he didn't make an appearance. Grandfather's truck was already backed up to the pigpen, and the loading chute was in place. The only thing left to do was to get the pigs up the chute into the truck. It was a task normally handled by Grandfather and Trixie. Loading pigs was a common occurrence on the hog farm. It was an easy job, and for the two of us, with or without Trixie, it should take only a few minutes.

Grandfather and I climbed over the boards into the pigpen. We herded the pigs into a bunch and slowly worked them towards the chute. At the bottom of the chute, however, the pigs stopped.

Suddenly one pig squealed and bolted. In an instant, there were pigs running in every direction. Grandfather and I gave chase, trying to head them off, but it was to no avail. There were pigs running in front of us. There were pigs running beside us. There were pigs running behind us. There were pigs running everywhere—everywhere, that is, except up the ruddy chute. We had charged around that pigpen too many times to count, before Grandfather finally stopped, exhausted. He was puffing like a steam engine as he took off his cap, pulled an old hanky out of his pocket, and wiped his brow. He never took his eyes off the pigs huddled together in a corner of the pen, away from the chute.

"Trixie!" Grandfather yelled. I could feel the urgency and the anger in his voice. Even I knew he had to get the pigs to town and time was running short. I also knew that Ma would be close to having lunch ready. Grandfather called again. "Trixie! Now, where's that dog when I need him?"

"Trixie! Here, boy!" I called out too. For it was painfully obvious that Grandfather needed more than my help to get this bunch of pigs into the truck. But Trixie didn't come. Grandfather was beside himself as once more he and I moved in on the pigs.

Then, for no apparent reason, those stupid pigs turned, and all together they ran—a mass of hogs moving forward as one—charging right between Grandfather and me, heading straight towards the chute. It was unbelievable! After all that chasing around, those pigs all tried to go up the chute, all of them together, at the same time. Unfortunately, the chute was not built to accommodate them all—it was a one-pig chute.

Grandfather immediately saw the impending danger. He spun around on his heels and wasted no time hustling up to the chute. He arrived at the chute just behind the pigs. Those pigs were squealing and grunting their fool heads off as they all tried to push their way into the chute at the same time. Grandfather was trying to get some of the pigs to back off before they broke the chute, but those pigs were a stubborn lot. In desperation Grandfather whipped the cap off his head and yelled and beat frantically on pigs' heads with his hat.

Suddenly one pig moved back, and one squeezed ahead. It broke free of the masses and started up the chute. A second pig was hot on his heels, trying to pass the first one. Boards creaked, groaned, and cracked. Nails squeaked as the charging pigs barged their way forward, severely testing the strength of the chute. The last pig finally made his way up the chute, and Grandfather breathed a sigh of relief.

"By George, Boy, it looks to me like I made a pretty good chute," he said. "I'm surprised that it held together."

"You sure do build good chutes, Grandfather," I said, agreeing with him.

"That's it, Boy. I think we've got 'em where we want 'em now. You get on up there and close the gate on the back of the truck before those pigs decide to come back down," Grandfather said.

I was halfway up the chute when we heard a grunt behind us. I stopped and looked around to the back of the pen, and then over to Grandfather. The look on Grandfather's face was priceless. He couldn't believe what he was seeing—there at the back of the pen, staring at the chute, stood a lone pig. In the confusion, neither Grandfather nor I had noticed that one pig had slipped away.

Once more, Grandfather and I moved around the

pen. The holdout moved ahead of us, walking slowly, until it reached the chute. There it stopped. It looked up the chute to the back of the truck, where its pigmates, although out of sight, were waiting. Then it turned to face Grandfather and me, and there it stood. With a grunt, that pig wiggled his nose in defiance. Because of that one pig, Grandfather was really going to be late. He was hungry and he was not happy.

Grandfather and I advanced, holding our arms out to make ourselves look bigger. But the pig stood its ground at the bottom of the chute. Its front feet were apart, braced. Its rump was pointing up the chute towards the stock rack. That pig was defiant and not going anywhere.

"Trixie!" Grandfather barked. At this point we could have used Trixie's pig-chasing abilities, but still Trixie did not come. "Look at that stupid pig. I always said the good Lord put the head on the wrong end of a pig. If the head was on the other end, that stupid pig would be going up the ramp instead of standing there staring at us. TRIXIE!" Grandfather bellowed, and then he muttered a few choice words that in no way should be used to describe the best dog in the world.

"Here, Trixie! C'mon, boy!" I called out, adding my voice to the plea for assistance.

"TRIXIE! C'mon, boy!" Grandfather called again to his little fox terrier.

Grandfather and I slowly moved a little closer to the pig that had its head on the wrong end.

"Sow pig!" Grandfather called out. He bent over a little farther and waved his arms.

"Sow pig!" I echoed. I, too, bent over and waved my arms harder.

Suddenly the pig squealed and charged. It came right at us—well, right at me anyway. It crashed into my leg as if I wasn't even there. I was knocked for a loop.

"Ow! Boy, those stupid pigs are sure solid," I complained to Grandfather, rubbing my leg. It hurt like crazy where that stupid pig with the head on the wrong end had slammed into me.

"Trixie!" Grandfather yelled again as he turned to chase that pig. Then, before I could add my two cents' worth, a white streak shot through the boards of the fence into the pigpen. Trixie, the smartest dog in the world, had finally arrived, full of energy, ready to go to work.

"Attaboy, go get 'im, Trixie!" Grandfather yelled happily. "Now we'll show that pig who's the boss around here."

With new-found energy, Grandfather charged after the pig with the head on the wrong end. Trixie took his cue from Grandfather. He bounded ahead and sank his needle-sharp teeth into the hock of the pig with the head on the wrong end.

"C'mon, Trixie! Let's go, boy! Let's get this stupid pig loaded!" I yelled. In the excitement of the chase, I forgot all about my throbbing leg.

There was no doubt that Trixie was in a pig-chasing mood, and he wasted no time in getting that pig moving. The pig was squealing like it had just been stabbed as it fled around the edge of the pen, trying to keep ahead of the dog. But Trixie was fast. He raced up alongside of the pig, nipping at its front leg until it turned. In a matter of seconds, Trixie had that pig running straight towards the chute.

"Attaboy, Trixie!" Grandfather cheered. "That's a good dog. Go git 'im, boy!"

As the pig-loading was coming to an end, I stopped to catch my breath and watch the final dash for the chute. That's when another problem presented itself: One of the pigs from the pack had moved to the back of the truck and was standing at the top of the chute. Now, I don't know if the pig with the head on the wrong end saw the other pig or not, but for whatever reason, at the bottom of the chute it suddenly turned and raced back across the pen.

Trixie had been hot on the hocks of the pig with the head on the wrong end, but when it suddenly turned, Trixie stopped. He had spotted the pig at the top of the chute. Trixie looked from one pig to the other. He was confused.

"C'mon, Trixie. Go git 'im, boy!"

Now, those were all the words of encouragement that Trixie needed. He knew instantly that he had been chasing the wrong pig. In a flash the smartest dog in the world forgot about the pig with the head on the wrong end.

"No, Trixie! No!" Grandfather bawled, as he realized the error that the best dog in the world was about to make. But Trixie ignored Grandfather's plea and dashed up that chute like a dog possessed.

"Trixie! No, Trixie, no!" Grandfather yelled, and he

too raced for the chute. "Git down here, you stupid dog!"

But Trixie was a dog on a mission. Up on the truck he found the motherlode of pigs. Trixie was in his glory. Fearlessly he charged forward. In an instant there were pigs squealing like crazy as they crowded together, pushing and shoving into the front of the stock rack, trying to escape. The boards of the rack were creaking and groaning as those hogs jammed into the corners. In no time flat, Trixie, the smartest dog in the world, had them pigs stirred to a frenzy.

"C'mon, Trixie!" Grandfather yelled angrily as he reached the bottom of the chute. "Git outta there!" But the pig-chasing mood had a solid grip on Trixie. He had a job to do and he was not about to leave those pigs until it was done. In short order the whole truck was rocking and bouncing as pigs pushed this way and that way, jumping from one side of the rack to the other to avoid the needle-sharp teeth. Trixie was having himself a grand old time.

"I suppose I'm gonna hafta go up there and drag that fool dog out by the tail," a very unhappy Grandfather said, snorting in disgust.

"If you're gonna grab something by the tail, you better grab a pig, then," I said to Grandfather, and I laughed, thinking that would be the funniest thing I ever saw. "Trixie doesn't have a tail. Remember, Grandfather, you cut if off when he was a puppy. Remember that, Grandfather?"

Grandfather didn't answer; he was too busy taking matters into his own hands. The pig with the head on the wrong end and I stood back and watched as Grandfather started up the chute. I had a feeling that if Grandfather got his hands on Trixie, that was one dog whose feet wouldn't be touching the chute on the way back down.

Grandfather had almost made it to the top of the chute when Trixie spotted him. In that instant he stopped his yipping and nipping and turned to look at Grandfather. The pigs that were crowded up at the front of the stock rack quit squealing and stood still. For a second or so there was not a sound. A calmness settled over Grandfather's hog farm. But not for long, because Grandfather being in the stock rack meant only one thing.

Trixie knew what it meant, but he got it all wrong as he reacted to his instincts. Now was really the time to move the pigs. He dashed at the pigs in the back of the truck. He jumped onto the mass of pork, and yipping and nipping like crazy, he raced across the backs of pigs all the way to the front of the rack. Somewhere along the way, however, the pigs separated, and Trixie, the best dog in the world, fell to the floor. Well, Trixie may have been down, but he was definitely not out. Amidst the legs and the hoofs, the little dog's muffled yipping and yapping could be heard. The squealing of the pigs became more intensive, testifying to the fact that down amongst all that pork, needle-sharp teeth were still testing pork hocks.

Instantly the grunting, squealing pigs exploded from the front of the stock rack. Grandfather, who had just reached the top of the chute, immediately stopped, but for only a second. He stared in horror at the mass of pork stampeding towards the back of the rack, the chute, and him. Those pigs were headed for the door at the top of the chute, and freedom. Grandfather just happened to be a minor obstacle in their way.

It was a sight to see when Grandfather jumped, or rather he dove — and it was not a graceful dive — sailing up and over the side of the chute. His arms and legs were flailing wildly as he landed face-first in a heap on the ground, but it was a moving heap, and he was scrambling on all fours, hands and knees, doing his best to get away from the back of that truck.

Meanwhile, up in the stock rack, those pigs all appeared to hit the door and the top of the chute at the same time. Nails popped and boards cracked, then snapped under the strain. The pig with the head on the wrong end and I just stood there watching the scene unfold. Now, I don't know what the pig with the head on the wrong end was thinking, but I could only stand and stare helplessly. The back of the stock rack just disintegrated into an avalanche of busted boards and squealing pigs. Pigs rolled down the chute. Pigs tumbled off the back of the truck. Grandfather's arms and legs were a blur as he scrambled to get out of the way of falling pigs.

Within seconds, the back of the truck was empty. Empty except for Trixie. That little dog stood there barking happily. There were pigs headed for the north pasture, there were pigs headed for the garden; one was headed for the house and another for the woodshed. There were pigs running in every direction.

I felt I should tell Grandfather that he was right—if the good Lord had put the head on the other end of those pigs, they'd all be running back to the truck instead of running away from it—but I held my tongue. Grandfather was in no mood for a joke.

Then, from the front step, Ma called. Her timing was impeccable.

"John! You can come in and eat now. Your lunch is ready."

"I haven't got time to eat, Girl!" Grandfather yelled back. "Can't you see that I'm busy?"

"Suit yourself," Ma replied. As she turned and walked back into the house, she added, "I'm ready to go to town whenever you are, John."

Suddenly I remembered that the pig with the head on the wrong end had bowled me over, and my leg really began to hurt. I limped towards the house and lunch.

"C'mon, Trixie!" Grandfather called as he began chasing pigs around the farm.

But Trixie, too, had heard the call for lunch and had lost interest in chasing pigs. He retired to the comfort of the front step. He stretched out and put his head down on his front paws and closed his eyes. After all, it was a job well done. Just another day in the life of a pigdog, the best dog in the world.

BOOBEE

"Yes sir, that snow is deep all right! It's right up to a well-digger's butt," I had heard Grandfather say. I didn't rightly know what a well-digger was, let alone how far up his butt went, but if a well-digger wasn't any taller than I was, then I would certainly agree with Grandfather's assessment. Yes, the snow that blanketed the countryside, including the Stump Farm, was very deep. It was mid-December, and I knew that whenever I strayed off the road or a beaten path, the snow was well past my butt.

Old Man Winter had come earlier than usual this year, and with him came the snow. Once he got started, it was as if that darn fool just didn't know when to stop. And if that wasn't bad enough, it was cold, really cold. In fact, it was so cold and there was so much snow that I was having a wee bit of difficulty getting out on my trapline to check my traps. However, it was not really the cold, nor the fact that the never-ending snow filled in my trail and I had to break a new trail every time I went out, that was causing me all the problems—it was Mom. Mom was the problem. She made it quite clear that in these weather conditions, the trapline was no place for man nor beast, let alone a young boy. Mom had laid down the law; and on the Stump Farm, even though I was "the man of the house", Mom's law ruled supreme.

On this evening, as was often the case in the winter, Grandfather stopped by to see how we were doing. Supper was over and I was glad, for it had been a quiet, solemn supper for the man of the house. Mom and I had had a little difference of opinion on how often a trapper should check his traps, and as usual, her opinion prevailed and my nose was out of joint.

With the exception of the stew pot, the table had been cleared and the dishes were almost finished when the door suddenly flew open and Grandfather burst in. He surveyed the kitchen, and his face lit up with a sly grin as he eyeballed the pot sitting in the middle of the table. After stomping his feet—and spraying snow across the kitchen floor—he plunked himself down in an empty chair beside the table. Then he leaned over and craned his neck for a better look into the pot.

"You're too late for supper, Grandfather," I said, feeling rather snarky. "Everything on the table has been devoured. The pot's empty."

"Don't you worry none about me, Boy. I've had my supper," Grandfather declared. He turned to Mom. "You wouldn't happen to have a drink to warm an old man's bones on such a cold night, would you, Girl?"

"Bobby, get your grandfather a cup of coffee," Mom said, and she gave me a look that said I had better move quickly and tread softly. She was obviously not very happy with me.

"Have you got a little something to warm the coffee?" Grandfather asked, and a devilish grin crossed his face.

"Oh, I think we might just have something," Mom said, and the devilish grin on Grandfather's face turned to a very satisfied smile.

"Gwen, would you put the cream and the sugar bowl back on the table for Grandfather," Mom said, and then she too flashed a mischievous grin. Grandfather's face suddenly lost its smile as he realized that Mom had just got him. Cream and sugar had not been what he had in mind.

"Here's your coffee, Grandfather," I said, placing the steaming-hot mug on the table in front of him.

"No no, Boy," Grandfather said in a disgusted voice, recoiling at the very thought of drinking coffee, "I haven't got time for coffee." He turned his attention to Mom. "I just stopped by to see how you were making out in this weather, Girl."

"Except for the deep snow and having to plow your way to everything, including the outhouse, we're doing fine," Mom replied.

"No we're not!" I snorted. "I wanted to go and check my trapline when I got home tonight, b-but Mom wouldn't let me." I knew that Grandfather would side with me on this issue; after all, a little snow never stopped a man from doing his chores. And tending the trapline was certainly one of my chores.

"Is that so, Boy?" Grandfather said.

"Yes, Grandfather, that's so," I said. "While we're sitting here jawin' about it, them squirrels is probably rotting away in my traps right now."

"You don't say," Grandfather said, shaking his head. "Well, I think your mother's right. I don't think it would be very wise to wander out in the bush in this weather, and certainly not in the dark. If I was you, I'd wait until the weekend, and go in the daylight. You know the bush is no place to be after dark in the wintertime. It's tough enough sluggin' it out in snow that deep when you can see where you're goin'. Your mother's right, Boy—you'd better wait till the weekend."

"Yeah, but I'll bet my traps are all full of squirrels," I grumbled.

"I don't think so, not in this weather," Grandfather said, shaking his head. Then he gave me a funny look and there was a twinkle in his eye. "Say, you remember Hubert's pet squirrel Boobee, don't you, Boy?"

"Uh-huh," I said, and my ears picked up.

"You know, Boy, I stopped by old Hubert's place on the way up here tonight, and he said he hasn't seen his squirrel in over a week now. Maybe it's just that it's too cold and nothin's movin' in the bush in this weather. Or maybe it's somethin' else. Tell me, Boy, you wouldn't be excited to check your traps just to see if maybe you'd bagged yerself a big squirrel, now, would you?"

My heart skipped a beat at the thought that Boobee might be doing more than hiding out in the cold weather. And I had made such an effort to avoid Boobee, too.

"That's right. Hubert said he hasn't seen his squirrel in over a week now," Grandfather said, and he looked me straight in the eye, waiting for an answer.

"I didn't trap Hubert's squirrel," I blurted out, trying to reassure Grandfather. At least not that I knew of, I thought. But if Boobee was missing, that was all the more reason that I should have been allowed to check my traps.

"I-I . . . I mean, I-I never even set my traps north of the house this year," I stuttered. "I'm missing out on some of my best squirrel trapping, just because of his squirrel."

Although Boobee was a wild squirrel and lived on the Stump Farm, he was Hubert's pet. Hubert had even trained him—well, he trained him to come into his shack and take peanuts off the table or out of your hand. And if you sat real still, and Boobee was in a good mood, he would even sit in the palm of your hand and eat the peanut. Oh, yes, I knew all about Boobee.

*   *   *

It was late in the fall the last time I had seen Boobee down at Hubert's place. I was sitting on a stump out in front of the old bachelor's shack, and Hubert and I were talking about the upcoming trapping season.

"Do you see many rabbits on your trapline?" Hubert asked.

"Oh, yeah, I see them all the time," I replied, "but Larry and I don't hunt them anymore. We got one last year, and Larry took it into the fur buyer. The old buyer acted like a skinned rabbit was a big deal, and because Larry had done such a good job on skinning and stretching it, he gave him a nickel. But it was really Dad who did all the work—he skinned it and stretched it. Then the fur dealer said that rabbits are only worth a penny and that's all he would pay in the future, so Dad said I couldn't shoot them anymore."

"I'll make you a better deal, Bobby. I'll give you a box of .22 shells for each rabbit you bring me," Hubert said. "How does that sound?"

"H-how does that sound?" I stammered, hardly able to believe my ears. Suddenly I had visions of bunnies scattered all around Hubert's shack and more .22 shells in my pockets than I had ever dreamed of. I chuckled. "I hope you got lots of .22 shells, Hubert. I know a good spot for rabbits, and I'm a crack shot, you know. I'll swamp you with rabbits."

"Don't you worry about that," Hubert replied. "You just remember, a box of .22 shells for every rabbit. Do we have a deal?"

"Do you want Dad to skin them, too?" I asked.

"They don't have to be skinned," Hubert said. "I just want them for my cats. They like rabbit."

About that time, over on the edge of the forest, a squirrel chattered.

"You bet we've got a deal," I said happily.

But old Hubert was now thinking about something else. He stood up and turned to face the pine trees on the north end of the Stump Farm.

"Here BOOBEE, BOOBEE!" Hubert called.

The squirrel chattered again, this time closer, and Hubert hustled into his shack. He returned very quickly, carrying a handful of peanuts.

"Here BOOBEE, BOOBEE!" he called again. "Shhh," he cautioned me, then he handed me a couple of peanuts and sat down.

We both watched the trees, and soon a red squirrel, the biggest red squirrel I had ever seen, scurried out of the forest and made a beeline for us. In one leap, that squirrel went from the ground up onto Hubert's knee. But Hubert had put the remaining peanuts in his pocket.

"Hold out a peanut, and let him see it," Hubert said to me. Now the squirrel was sitting on his shoulder, checking him out. I did as I was told. I held out the peanut and called.

"Here, Boobee!" That squirrel never even hesitated when he saw that the peanut was in my hand. In one leap he left Hubert's shoulder, barely touching his knee before hitting the ground, and in another leap he was on my knee. He jumped from my knee into the palm of my hand and picked up the peanut. I watched in silence as Boobee sat on his haunches right in the palm of my hand. He held the peanut in his front paws and went to work. His little teeth flashed as he snapped the shell off the peanut, and in a second he devoured the two nuts inside.

I never took my eyes off that little rascal. Not because I was surprised, or because I had never seen Boobee before (I had), but now the trapping season was getting close. Soon the squirrels would be prime. As far as squirrels went, Boobee was definitely a prize — big and fat, he was a giant among squirrels. I could only stare longingly at Boobee.

I left Hubert's place and raced home. I couldn't wait to get out and shoot some rabbits, but every time I started to think about rabbits, that darned Boobee popped into my head. I was lucky that Grandfather was not butchering one of his pigs; I had been able to keep his .22. I got the .22 off the gun rack. After all, if I was going to shoot a rabbit, I needed a gun in good working order. But all I could think about was that giant squirrel. I dusted off the .22 and I oiled the barrel and polished the stock. On one end of a piece of string I tied a nail; on the other end I made a loop and inserted a small piece of cloth. I put a couple of drops of oil on the cloth, then I dropped the string nail-end-first down the barrel and pulled the string and the cloth through. When I held that gun up to my eye and stared through the barrel, it shone like brand-new. But it was not a rabbit I saw at the other end, it was that darn squirrel. For some reason, I had Boobee on the brain.

"Those old squirrels — I mean rabbits — will never know what hit them this year," I chuckled. I could already see myself collecting umpteen boxes of shells. Yes, old Hubert had no idea what he had let himself in for.

Next I went out to the woodshed. My squirrel traps

were hanging on a nail at the back of the shed. I took them down and checked each one to make sure they were in perfect working condition. I was leaving nothing to chance this season. Normally I wouldn't get this motivated until I was sure the squirrels were prime, but seeing Boobee had triggered me to action. There would be no place for squirrels or bunnies to hide from me this year.

Once the traps were ready, I turned my attention to my squirrel stretchers, and was just looking at the biggest one when somebody entered the woodshed and cast a shadow over me. I turned to look at my visitor.

"Hi, Grandfather," I said, looking up from my stretchers.

"I see you're gettin' a jump on the trappin' season, Boy," Grandfather said. He smiled broadly as he walked over and took the big stretcher from my hand. "This looks like a pretty big stretcher for a little squirrel!" he added.

"Yeah," I replied, "it is, but this year there's some mighty big squirrels out there, an' — well, I wanna be all ready to go as soon as them squirrels are prime. But I'm gonna shoot me some rabbits first. Old Hubert offered me a box of .22 shells for each rabbit I bring him. And Dad don't even have to skin them, because Hubert's just gonna feed 'em to his dumb cats."

"That's what he tells me," Grandfather said. "He also tells me that you were down to his place and you fed his pet squirrel. Is that right?"

"That's right, Grandfather," I replied. "Boy, that Boobee is sure one big squirrel, too. Did you see him, Grandfather? He must have got big from eating all those peanuts. You know, I'll bet I could get a dollar for his hide!"

"Yeah, Boy, that's what Hubert figured you was thinkin'," Grandfather said.

"He was? Why'd he think something like that?" I asked, sounding surprised and innocent.

"You know, Boy," Grandfather said, "Hubert may be old, but he's not dumb." His voice had taken on a very serious tone. It was not often I heard that tone in Grandfather's voice, but I sure heard it that day. "He can read a man pretty good, and he just figured, by the way you was sizin' up that squirrel, that you were measurin' him up for a stretcher. You know, a big stretcher, something like this one right here. Now, you weren't measurin' Hubert's pet up for a stretcher, were you, Boy?"

"Me? No . . . no," I mumbled. I took the big stretcher he was holding and leaned it against the wall.

"That's good," Grandfather said. Then he added in a very stern voice, "You know, Boy, if something was to happen to Hubert's pet squirrel, I—well, you know, Boy, I've got a lot of pigs to butcher and . . . and I might just be needin' my .22 back for the rest of the winter."

"B-but Grandfather, that's not fair! You know them squirrels, they travel all over the bush. An-and some of my best squirrel dens are in the spruce trees just south of Hubert's place. Boobee could be anywhere."

"I know, Boy," Grandfather said, "I know. And it

would be too bad if that squirrel suddenly disappeared, particularly in the trapping season."

There was no mistaking Grandfather's meaning. I was going to have to change my trapline. The spruce and pine trees on the north end of the Stump Farm were out of bounds. Boobee needed to be safe, from me. I was taking no chances—I couldn't afford to lose the .22.

*   *   *

The day after Grandfather's visit, I couldn't get Boobee off my mind. I decided that I would take matters into my own hands. Cold and snow, Mom's law or no law, this day would be different. Today, or I should say tonight, was when my trapline had to be run.

I was starting to have second thoughts about the traps I had set out behind the barn. It just might be that they were too close to the farm buildings and to the old bachelor. I hadn't slept all night, thinking about that dumb squirrel. I had to make sure that Boobee hadn't wandered into one of my traps. He may have been trained, but he wasn't that smart, and he just might have been harvested. Thus, it was time. It was time that I, being the man of the house, took control of my destiny and exercised my authority. This evening, right after school, Mom's law or no Mom's law, my traps would all be checked. I had made up my mind.

As I had done on so many afternoons before, I charged out of the red brick schoolhouse. I raced down the South Road as fast as my little legs would carry me.

Well, that is, I hurried . . . or rather, I tried to hurry, following the single vehicle track that snaked along the South Road. In many places, the track was already covered with snow; but undaunted, I plowed my way down the South Road towards the Stump Farm.

By the time I reached Nick-the-Dog-Man's place I was puffing like a steam engine. There I stopped and held my breath, and I listened. My heart was beating so hard it felt like a drum booming in my ears. I prayed that those stupid dogs wouldn't hear the thumping of my heart or the pounding in my ears. Standing in the gathering dusk (in December it was always dark before I got home from school) in the bitterly cold air of a mid-winter's eve, steam rose from my sweating body and drifted up in front of my face. Every little hair of the fur that lined the fringe of my parka hood was coated with frost. It felt like my face was peering through a white halo.

The South Road was strangely silent, but there was something in the air. The hair on the back of my neck was trying to stand on end. I'm sure that if it hadn't been for my parka hood, my hair would have bristled out like the quills on a porcupine's back. The feeling was always there when I arrived at this section of the South Road. I knew what it was, but I couldn't help myself. It was Nick-the-Dog-Man's dogs. In the dusk the spruce trees along the side of the road took on ominous, shadowy shapes, and I had this horrible feeling that those puppies were hiding behind the trees. I listened, real hard, and I was certain I could hear those puppies breathing, licking their chops, as they crouched in the shadows. I could even feel the muscles in their legs — tense, like coiled springs — waiting, just waiting to pounce on me.

But I could not dally, I didn't have time to waste playing silly games with Nick-the-Dog-Man's dogs. Dogs or not, tonight I had a mission. My trapline was calling; I had to press on.

As quietly as I could, I pushed onward, plowing through the snow on the far side of the road, away from the lone vehicle track. I moved slowly, silently, afraid to breathe, for I really didn't want to disturb those puppies. The going was tough enough without having those stupid dogs nipping at your heels.

"Whew!" I said, and I breathed a sigh of relief. I was one happy guy when I reached the corner of the fence that separated Grandfather's farm from Nick-the-Dog-Man's place. I couldn't help feeling proud of myself, for once again I had sneaked by those dogs. Oh man, but I was pretty good, and I knew that this was going to be my lucky day.

But first I had to let Nick-the-Dog-Man's dogs know that I had outsmarted them again. Triumphantly, I lifted my nose to the sky, and the falling snow, and I opened my mouth.

"Arrrooooo," I howled at the top of my lungs. To me, the sound of my voice on this frigid winter evening was like that of a wolf baying at the moon. "Take that, you stupid dogs! Arrrooooo."

Instantly hundreds of dogs took up the challenge. Some joined the serenade and they too howled; some barked; some yelped and whined; others snarled and growled. I turned and ran for my life. I raced away as fast as I could, plowing through the snow. Down the South Road I ran, heading for the safety of the Stump Farm. Behind me, those puppies were creating quite a racket, yipping and yapping as loud as they could. But I never looked back. I never even turned around to look at the chaos I had caused. I knew what was there. Out on the road in front of Nick-the-Dog-Man's place there would be a swarm of his puppies, and they would all be looking for some heels to nip at.

"Don't worry about supper for me, I haven't got time to eat," I called to Mom as I charged through the door of the log house. I kicked off my boots and ran to my bedroom to get my hunting bag.

"Not so fast, young man," Mom said as I charged back into the kitchen.

"I haven't got time," I snapped at her. But she was standing in my way, barring the door.

"My goodness, Bobby, you're all flushed! Are you sick?" Mom asked. That comment stopped me, and I quickly looked at her. I could see the look of concern on her face as she reached over and put her hand on my forehead.

"Me? Of course I'm all right! I'm fine," I replied.

"My word, Bobby, your forehead is hot! You're burning up! You've got a fever, and just look at you — you're wringing wet!" she exclaimed.

"It's okay, I'm fine, Mom," I protested. "I'm just sweating a little. I ran all the way from school and now — now, I'm gonna go and check my trapline."

"Y-you . . . you're gonna do what?" Mom asked, as

if she couldn't believe what she had just heard. She stood there for a second and she looked at me like I had gone daft.

"I haven't got time to waste standing here chinwagging with you, Mom. I'm gonna check my trapline!" I stated emphatically. After all, I knew that if I was going to exert my authority as the man of the house, I was going to have to be firm. But it didn't take Mom long to gather her wits about her.

"You'll do nothing of the sort, young man," Mom stated. She stepped forward and looked me straight in the eye. "You just march yourself right into your bedroom and put on a dry shirt. Then you can run outside and do your chores. It's going to be another cold one tonight, and since you've got so much energy, you can split some extra wood and bring that into the house too."

"But Mom," I protested (I could feel my authority slipping away fast), "I need to go and check my traps. I'll bet they're full of squirrels. And—and I didn't tell you, but I think my traps in the spruce trees behind the barn may be too close to the buildings."

"You've always set your traps in that stand of spruce," Mom said. "They haven't been too close to the buildings before, have they?"

"No," I mumbled, "I just have to go and check them, that's all."

"It's dark and it's too cold," Mom said. "Anyway, the squirrels have more sense than to be out in weather like this. Now, you change your shirt and get your chores done before supper. The traps can wait until the weekend, like they do every week. Then you can check them."

"But—"

"No more buts, young man! You're not going out on that trapline at this hour of the night, and certainly not in this weather," Mom stated firmly. "Now go and get a dry shirt on, and do your chores."

"It's not too cold for squirrels, Mom! Th-they even got fur coats a-and they're used to being out in the cold," I argued in vain.

"That's enough!" Mom snapped, invoking her brand of law once again. "Now, change your shirt and go do your chores, like you're told."

"Oh sure, it's too cold to check my traps, but it isn't too cold to go to school and it isn't too cold to do chores," I grumbled as I stomped out of the room.

What started out to be such a great day was rapidly turning into a lousy one, and it was going from bad to worse. Carrying the lantern, I stormed out of the house. The snow had almost covered the trail from the house to the barn. I plowed forward, and as I neared the well, I stepped on a clump of frozen snow, an ice ball that had formed when someone stupidly dumped water from the water bucket. My foot no sooner hit that ruddy chunk of ice than my ankle turned, and I lost my balance. I tried my best to get the other foot moving, but it was useless in the deep snow; that foot was planted solidly. I twisted my body around as best I could to keep the lantern high and dry as I plowed headfirst into the snow.

I grumbled and I cursed as I led the cows and horses

from the barn to the watering trough. I continued my tirade as I pulled water out of the well and dumped it into the trough. But I laughed when I caught the pail on the corner of the well and dumped half of the water into the snow. There, I thought—another ice ball, for someone else to trip over. My grumpy mood returned as I milked the cows. I even scolded the cats as I aimed a few squirts of milk in their direction.

"If you stupid cats weren't so lazy, you'd catch yourselves a mouse, and I wouldn't have to feed you every time I milked the cows," I snarled. But the cats only meowed and purred. I missed their saucer, but they ignored me as they lapped the milk from the floor.

My mood hadn't improved a whole lot by the time I carried the lantern into the woodshed and hung it on a hook. Right beside the lantern was a reminder of what I really should have been doing. It was the birdcage where I stored my squirrels until Dad came home to skin them. However, the cage was empty, a sad testimony to my trapping ability, not to mention Mom's law.

I set about chopping firewood, swinging the axe with a vengeance at each block of wood. Splinters flew as the frozen blocks split easily. Larry arrived home and carried every piece into the house.

Finally Saturday arrived. As soon as my chores were done, I grabbed Grandfather's .22, slung my knapsack on my back, and headed for the bush. My trapline beckoned. I could already feel the weight of the knapsack full of squirrels on my back as I headed out the door.

The snow on the path to the barn was deep enough, but it was nothing compared to the snow I encountered when I stepped off the path at the barn. The old trail marking my trapline was completely gone, hidden under a couple of feet of new snow. The snow was right up to my waist as I plowed forward, heading for the first clump of spruce. The trees were only a hundred yards from the barn, but I was puffing by the time I reached them. This stand of trees was the closest to Hubert's place that I had set a trap; if Boobee was to get caught, this was the place. The walking was much easier under the trees, and I was able to move around quite quickly and check my traps. To say I was disappointed would be an understatement. Each trap was exactly where I had left it, hidden in a cubby, still set. The only consolation was that Boobee was definitely not caught.

The trip around the trapline should have taken me no more than a couple of hours, three at the most. But plowing through the heavy snow had slowed me down. It was well past lunch, and I was hungry and dead tired by the time I reached the South Road. I had checked only about half of my traps and I did not have a single squirrel to show for my efforts, although I did bag a rabbit for Hubert's cats. After all that plowing through the snow I needed a rest, so I detoured from my trapline to deposit the bunny with Hubert and collect my box of .22 shells. I figured the remaining traps could wait for another day.

I was really pooped by the time I dragged the bunny and myself into Hubert's place. I don't know how, but he must have known I was out on my trapline.

101

"Come in, Bobby!" he called before I had even knocked. "Come in. Sit down and warm yourself. You must be tired from walking through all that deep snow. Would you like some hot tea?"

"No, thanks," I replied. "It's getting late, and I have to get home. If I'm lucky I might even make it in time to do my chores. I didn't finish checking my traps, but I did get you a rabbit."

"I know," he said, and smiled. "It's tough walking when the snow is so deep. And thank you for bringing me the rabbit for my cats. Your box of shells is right there on the table." And it was, too. Sitting on the table all by itself was a single box of .22 shells.

"What would you have done if I had two rabbits?" I asked.

"But you didn't, you just brought one," he said. The old bachelor just smiled knowingly.

"I-I didn't get any squirrels," I said. "In fact, I didn't even see any. Grandfather said you hadn't seen Boobee around. I just want you to know that I didn't catch him."

"I know," Hubert said, and he smiled again.

"You do? You know that too? I mean . . . I mean, h-how did you know that?" I asked. Man, this was spooky! Was it just me, or did that old bachelor know everything that went on around the Stump Farm?

"Oh, Boobee was here. He came for his peanut today," Hubert said. "He might even still be here."

"Really?" I said. "Y-you mean he's out—out in this weather? B-but I never even saw a squirrel track all day."

"I'll call him," Hubert said. He gave me a peanut, and he took one, then he walked over to the door. "BOOBEE! BOOBEE!" he called.

In the distance a squirrel chattered, and in a few minutes the giant squirrel appeared, just as he always did whenever Hubert called. The squirrel seemed to be as light as a feather, bouncing across the top of the snow, coming for his peanut.

I couldn't believe it. In this cold weather, that squirrel showed up. I watched as he took the peanut from Hubert, but he didn't sit around to eat it. Instead, clutching his treat in his teeth, he took off—and my heart skipped a beat. He didn't go back the way he came. I watched as he bounced away through the pine trees. The giant squirrel was headed south towards one of my unchecked traps. Towards disaster.

I didn't even say goodbye to old Hubert; I bolted out of his shack and I too headed south, through the deep snow, after that stupid squirrel. As I had learned earlier in the day, I was not as light as a feather, and I did not bounce along on the top of the snow. I sank right down to ground level. I was up to my waist in snow and moving as fast as I could to catch up to the squirrel. I kept hoping that he would stop and eat the peanut so I could get ahead of him, but I had no such luck. It didn't appear to me that the squirrel had even slowed down as he raced towards his doom.

My heart was beating like a trip-hammer in no time at all, and it got worse as both the squirrel and I got closer to the stand of spruce where I knew the deadly trap lay hidden, just waiting for an unsuspecting squirrel. I had rushed along as hard and as fast as I could, and I thought I was going to pass out by the time I reached the spruce trees. At least under the spruce trees the snow wasn't as deep, and there I could move a little faster. It seemed as if that squirrel had a date with my trap, for his tracks hadn't wavered off-course even an inch all the way from Hubert's place to the spruce trees. And now the tracks were still heading straight towards the trap.

I was really tired. I was panting and sweating like crazy, and my whole body was aching by the time I came around the spruce tree where my trap was set. At that moment, I think my heart stopped beating, for it was at the cubby where my trap was set that the last squirrel track appeared in the snow. I couldn't even bring myself to look inside, for I knew what was there, and I knew it was the end of Grandfather's .22 for me.

Then, to my surprise, from the tree above my head a squirrel chattered, scolding me for being so close to his den. I looked up and there sat Boobee, eating the peanut that Hubert had given him. If I could have reached him, I think that I would have kissed that squirrel.

I squatted down and reached for a twig to spring the trap with, and at that moment I realized that I was still holding the peanut Hubert had given me back at his shack. I also realized that my hands were pretty darned cold, because in my haste to catch up to the squirrel, I had left my mitts back at Hubert's. I dropped the twig, stood up, and held my hand out.

"BOOBEE! BOOBEE!" I called, holding the peanut

out for the squirrel to see. But he ignored me; he just sat there on a branch and chewed the peanut he already had.

Since Boobee was straying this far from the old bachelor's place, I knew I had to remove the trap. Thanks to the giant squirrel, my trapline was growing ever smaller. I picked up another short twig and squatted down on my haunches again to get a better look into the cubby. I aimed the twig at the pan — the trigger that would spring the trap — and slowly I leaned over, thrusting the twig forward. Then all hell broke loose.

Just at that moment, the stupid squirrel decided that he wanted the peanut I had offered him. I heard a faint scratch on the bark above my head, and the next thing I knew, the squirrel took a flying leap at me and landed right smack dab on my shoulder. Needless to say, the sudden appearance of a live ball of fur next to my head scared the dickens right out of me. My first reaction was to brush him off, but the squirrel had other ideas. He had seen the peanut in my hand, and he had seen me put my hand into the cubby. In a flash he was racing down my arm, towards my hand and the cubby, where the trap was still very much alive and dangerous. Instinctively, I shook my arm violently, to rid myself of the critter. But Boobee was bound and determined to get into that cubby and retrieve his peanut. At about the same time as Boobee stuck his head into the cubby, I jammed my hand in a little further.

Now, there wasn't enough room in the cubby for the trap, the twig to spring it, my hand, and the giant squirrel. The cubby exploded. Dried twigs, moss, and grass flew in every direction. The distinctive sound of frozen metal on frozen metal, the steel jaws of the trap slamming shut, rang out loud and clear on that winter day.

"No!" I yelled, and my heart stopped as I looked at Boobee thrashing around in the tangle of twigs that had been my cubby. There was blood splattered all over the snow, the twigs, and Boobee. At the same time I felt a numbness in my finger. Boobee scrambled free of the debris and scampered up the nearest spruce tree.

"Oh, no!" I screeched when I realized what had really happened. The blood on the ground was not from Boobee—it was mine. The steel jaws of my trap had snapped shut right on the end of my finger.

I felt a burning pain shoot up through my half-frozen hand. I yanked my hand out of the cubby and stared at the end of my finger. The steel jaws had just grazed me, but they had caught enough so that I ended up losing a good piece of skin. Blood shot out the end of the finger, and I cursed and jumped to my feet. I didn't even take the time to hang the sprung trap in the tree as I raced out of the spruce trees.

Somewhere behind me, from high in the safety of a spruce tree, there was more scolding chatter. While I clutched my injured hand and bolted for home, Boobee sat in a tree complaining that I had welched on the deal. In all the confusion, I had forgotten to leave him his peanut.

"JUST SAY 'SHOO', BOY!"

I stuck my tongue out the side of my mouth, then I screwed up my face and pursed my lips, just the way Grandfather had told me.

"Shoo! Shoo!" I bellowed at the top of my lungs as I charged around the corner of the old log house. "Shoo!"

The old yellow dog I had spotted sneaking down the driveway towards the house didn't hesitate for even a fraction of a second. He was a blur of yellow hair as he spun around, tucked his tail tightly between his hind legs, which were pumping like pistons, and dug deep furrows into the packed snow as he clawed for traction.

"Yahoo!" I screamed for all on the South Road to hear. "Grandfather was right. Look at that yellow dog go!" I stood at the side of the house looking at the empty driveway and the dogless South Road. Yes, Grandfather had been right. The events as they unfolded today were a far cry from what they had been last week. I smiled as I thought back. . . .

*　　*　　*

"Shoo. G'wan! Git home! Git outta here, you mangy mutt!" I yelled angrily. I waved my arms wildly as I ran, then I stopped and kicked up a cloud of snow as I tried desperately to shoo the mongrel away from our place. But he was a wily old cuss. I couldn't get near him. He stayed just far enough away, just out of harm's way.

The big yellow dog had staked his territory in our driveway and about a hundred yards of the South Road on either side of our driveway. He had been around for so long that he had turned just about every lump, bump, and chunk of snow yellow. Larry and I had tried everything we knew, short of shooting that dog, to chase it away, but he was not about to leave. Oh, I would have gladly shot him, but Mom wouldn't let me. In fact she wouldn't even let me carry Grandfather's .22 out on my trapline to shoot squirrels or chickens ever since that darn dog had showed up at the Stump Farm.

It wasn't that the yellow dog was hungry or looking for a new home—it was that our little fox terrier bitch, Bunny, was the object of his attentions. Bunny was just a little bit of a dog, not much bigger than a rabbit and less than half the size of the yellow dog. Bunny was actually my sister Judy's dog. But Judy, knowing how badly I wanted a dog, had been so kind as to give me half of her dog. The back half. And it was my half of the dog that this big yellow dog (he looked about the size of a St. Bernard) was interested in. Bunny was in season, looking for a boy dog, and the big yellow dog had more than a passing interest in her.

Larry and I had planned and schemed to get rid of that dog, but to no avail. When we were in the house, the big yellow dog would come right up to the door, and whine and scratch. It was an invitation to Bunny to come out, but it was Larry or myself who would end up charging through the door. The yellow dog would jump back to safety and keep his distance. Often we raced all the way to the South Road chasing him, but he just pranced along in front of us, with his tail held high in a curl over his back. I'm sure that old dog was just laughing at us. He was not too worried about two little boys yelling, shouting, waving their arms, and throwing snowballs. No, nothing we could do was about to discourage that old yellow dog.

Mom wasn't very happy about the big yellow dog hanging around either. She had a lot of work to do, and looking after Bunny when we were at school was just another unwelcome chore. She had to go outside and wait every time she let Bunny out. Mom was even less pleased with the big dog's calling card. The yellow spots on the snow were increasing daily, and they increased in number as they got closer to our front door.

The yellow snow, the big old yellow dog's calling card, had not gone unnoticed.

109

"Say, Girl, looks to me like you got a whole pack of dogs paintin' up the snow on your driveway and in your yard," Grandfather pointed out, laughing.

As he often did in the winter, he had stopped by for a cup of coffee. The coffee was just an excuse; it was Grandfather's way of checking on us when Dad was away. He was sitting at the table, and a big puddle of water was forming on the linoleum where the snow was melting off his boots. Grandfather never took his boots off. I think he figured it was easier for someone else to mop up the floor than for him to bend over and undo the snaps.

"Just one," Mom sighed, and she motioned for me to mop up the floor around his feet. "Just one. It's that big old yellow dog. I'm sick and tired of that mutt hanging around. Bobby and Larry have tried everything to chase him away, but he won't leave."

"Yeah, Grandfather," I said, adding my two cents' worth as I swished the old mop around and over his boots. "Larry and me, we chase him out of the yard every day, but he just follows us right back in. He's after Bunny, you know."

"Is that right, Boy?" Grandfather said, and a sly smile tickled the corners of his lips.

"Yeah, that's right, Grandfather," I snorted. "Me and Larry, we done everything we could, but he won't leave."

"Maybe you're not holding your mouth right, Boy," Grandfather replied, looking more serious.

"What do you mean?" I asked.

"Did you hold your mouth like this, Boy?" I

110

watched as Grandfather screwed up his face, then pursed his lips and stuck his tongue out the side of his mouth. It was a look I had seen many times before, but only when Grandfather was working at a particularly tough chore. I had to admit, when Grandfather stuck his tongue out that side of his mouth he looked pretty serious, like he really meant business.

"I don't think I held my mouth like that," I replied. "You know, I don't remember how I held my mouth." Then I tried to screw up my face, stick my tongue out the side of my mouth, and purse my lips. "Is this right, Grandfather?" I mumbled.

"Thanks for the coffee, Girl," Grandfather said. He completely ignored me. "I'll see if there's anything I can do about that dog," he added when he had finished his coffee.

"Do you want your .22, Grandfather?" I asked. "I'll bet you could get rid of him with that."

"I don't think so, Boy," Grandfather replied. "That yellow dog probably belongs to somebody, maybe even a little boy. You wouldn't like it if somebody shot your dog, now, would you?"

"I only got half a dog," I said, reminding him of the facts, "and my half a dog isn't turning somebody else's snow all yellow and scratching at their door and whining all the time."

Larry and I followed Grandfather outside. To our surprise, he didn't even look at the big yellow dog, but the big yellow dog looked at him. Just like he did for us, he pranced away down the driveway, his tail held proudly in a curl up over his back. He stayed just far enough away so that he couldn't be hit by a snowball. Larry and I charged after that dog and chased him all the way to the South Road. But Grandfather hadn't followed us, and when I looked around he was gone. Larry and I stayed at the road. We screamed at the dog, "Shoo! G'wan, git outta here, you mangy mutt!"

The snow on the South Road had recently been plowed, and the grader had left a ridge of caked snow chunks right down the middle of the road. We didn't have to make snowballs; instead, we picked up chunks of packed snow and with all our might we threw them at that old yellow dog. I even practiced sticking my tongue out the side of my mouth, like Grandfather had showed me. I did it every time I threw a snowball; however, I obviously wasn't holding it just right, because that stupid yellow dog just sat on his haunches and looked at us from a safe distance, just beyond where our snowballs were landing.

"That's no way to get a dog to go home, Boy," Grandfather said as he suddenly reappeared. "Just say 'shoo', Boy! 'Shoo!' — and that old yellow dog will head for home as fast as his legs will carry him."

"Humpf," I snorted. "That I'd like to see. We've said everything and tried everything, but that stupid dog doesn't have a clue that he's not wanted around here."

"Okay, Boy," Grandfather said, smiling. "Just stand back, Boy, and let me show you how it's done."

"Here, boy!" Grandfather called to the old yellow dog, and he held one hand out in front of him.

Larry and I stood there dumbfounded. Grandfather wasn't even trying to scare that old yellow dog. Instead, he was calling him, in the same gentle tone we always used to call Bunny. The old yellow dog got up off his haunches, cocked his head to one side, and gave Grandfather a curious look.

"How to go, Grandfather!" Larry said. "We've been trying to get rid of him, and you want to make friends. I don't think we need your kind of help. Mom will kill us if we bring that dog back to the house."

"You just let me worry about that, Boy," Grandfather replied. "We're gonna git rid of him, Boy. But first we have to get his attention, and then we're gonna give him a little kick-start. You watch, Boy, that yellow dog will be only too happy to tuck his tail between his legs and hightail it for home when I'm finished with him!" Grandfather chuckled. I had my doubts, though, because Grandfather wasn't holding his tongue just right. He didn't look too serious to me.

"Here, puppy. C'mon, boy!" Grandfather called. "Wheeet, wheeet, wheeet!" he whistled.

But that big old yellow dog was pretty smart, and very leery. He must have recognized that Grandfather was no little kid who just waved his arms, shouted, kicked, and threw snow.

"We've throwed a lot of stuff at him," I said to Grandfather. "I don't think he'll come to you."

"Well, Boy, I guess you'll just have to back down the driveway a ways, then. You've probably got him all riled up," Grandfather said. "I bet that old dog just needs some tender lovin' care. He'll come to me, all right. You back away, now, boys."

As Larry and I backed away, Grandfather moved

113

slowly down the South Road towards the yellow dog, and he continued to sweet-talk as he inched his way forward. Well, there was no doubt about it, Grandfather did have a way with animals. It didn't take much coaxing, and soon Grandfather had that old yellow dog down crawling on his belly, coming to him. The dog was whining happily; and his big old tail, curled up over his back, was wagging from side to side so hard that I thought for sure it was going to fly right off.

"C'mon, boy. That's a good dog," Grandfather cooed tenderly, encouraging the dog to come even closer.

And the dog was coming—closer and closer he came. It seemed to me that he wanted to run right up there and lick Grandfather's face; but he was cautious, approaching slowly, crawling on his belly and whining. His tail never stopped wagging; his tongue kept licking both sides of his chops, and his head bobbed up and down and side to side. The dog was coming nearer Grandfather, and the closer he came the more he was submitting to a superior, the dominant male. Grandfather never stopped talking, and finally that old yellow dog was right in front of him, close enough to touch. The dog stretched forward and tentatively licked the extended hand. Grandfather allowed him to lick the hand for a second or two, then he scratched him on the side of the head, then the ears and the neck. Suddenly the yellow dog rolled over on his back, and Grandfather reached forward and scratched his belly. The dog was ecstatic—after a week of having people throw everything but the kitchen sink at him, here was a friend. His big tail was wagging, throwing snow in every direction. He whined and squirmed around like he was about to turn inside out.

"How to go, Grandfather!" I snorted in disgust. "You got him where you want him now. Now that you got him kick-started, you just say 'shoo', Grandfather. I'll bet he can't wait to hear you say that. Look at him crawling around your feet—he's dying to hear those words so he can head for home."

Anybody could see that Grandfather and that old yellow dog were the best of friends. Even the dog just knew he had been accepted into our pack. He bounced to his feet and crowded closer around his new friend, the leader of the pack, the alpha male. He jumped up on Grandfather and tried to lick his face.

"Man, there's no way we're ever going to get rid of that mangy mutt now," I said to Larry. "Just look! Grandfather, he sure has a funny way of scaring him."

"Yeah, he sure looks like he's scared silly to me," Larry replied, sounding as disgusted as I was. We could only stand there and watch as all of our efforts for the past week were going down the drain.

"Are you holding your tongue just right, Boy?" Grandfather called back to us as he continued to play with the dog. I thought that he had forgotten all about us.

"Hrumpf!" I snorted disgustedly. I had quit practicing that a long time ago. We were trying our best to get rid of that dog, and now Grandfather was making a pet of him.

"Now listen, Boy, when I yell 'shoo', you both holler

'shoo', and you wave your hands and come running up here as fast as you can," Grandfather called to us again. "Are you ready now, Boy?"

"Sure, Grandfather," Larry and I both mumbled together. "We yell and wave our hands and arms, and run up to you like a couple of idiots." We are a couple of idiots, I thought, as I watched Grandfather play with that stupid dog. How were we ever going to get rid of that dog now? He thinks Grandfather is his best friend.

"You just watch, Boy, and you do as I tell you. Are you ready?"

"Yeah, we're watching," we grumbled. "We're ready."

Suddenly we knew that Grandfather was serious: His face was all screwed up. His lips were pursed and his tongue was sticking out the side of his mouth. In the bat of an eye, he pulled his other hand out of his pocket. He flipped that dog over on his back and rubbed his belly some more. But the hand he took out of his pocket he rubbed under that old yellow dog's tail, and he gave it a good twist. At the same time Grandfather yelled.

"SHOO! SHOO, DOG, SHOO!"

A single loud, sharp yip escaped from the throat of the surprised dog. In a flash the old yellow dog was on his feet. He didn't seem to know what to do. He spun right around, and his hind legs collapsed. He bared his teeth and tried to nip at his butt. He yipped, then he spun around the other way and tried to nip at the other side. He turned this way and that trying to get a good look at his butt, to see what or who was hanging onto it — but there was only his tail there. It was about that

116

time, I think, that the big old yellow dog got the real message. There was something dreadfully wrong with his butt.

Everything happened so fast, and Larry and I were so surprised, that we forgot to yell and wave our arms and charge towards Grandfather and the yellow dog. We both stood there watching, like a couple of dolts.

"Yell, Boy!" Grandfather hollered. "C'mon, Boy, yell and chase him home."

"Shoo!" Larry and I both screamed at the top of our lungs. "Shoo!" Then we both ran towards Grandfather, screaming, waving our arms, and kicking up a snowstorm.

Yes, that big old yellow dog had got the message. He didn't need any more encouragement than what Grandfather had given him.

Yip! Yip! Yip! Yip! wailed the yellow dog as Grandfather's message began to sink in. As Larry and I charged forward, the yellow dog took off down the road at a dead run. He didn't go far before he spun around again and tried to nip his butt. Then he dropped his butt right onto the snow ridge left by the snowplow; his hind legs shot forward, and with his hind paws up around his ears, his front legs clawed frantically at the packed snow as he tore off down the road. That big old yellow dog was digging for home as hard and as fast as his front legs could pull his back end over the ridge of packed snow.

Larry and I looked on in amazement, while Grandfather stood there with a knowing smile, the smile of a job well done. We watched as the yellow dog

117

disappeared from sight, never slowing down one little bit.

"Holy mackerel! What did you do, Grandfather?" I asked. "Boy, that old yellow dog was sure flying when he left here."

"I don't think that old yellow dog will bother you no more," Grandfather said. "And if he should happen to show up here again, you just remember what I told you — you just say 'shoo', Boy, and I'll bet that dog will turn and hightail it for home."

Then Grandfather turned and walked away along the South Road, heading for home. For a moment, I thought I got a whiff of turpentine as he walked past me.

BARRACK BOX SNAKE

Dear Mom and family:

It was the same greeting that I put at the start of every letter home. I doubt that my letters were any different from those of most of the cadets in Vernon, although I was surprised that some cadets didn't write any letters at all. Letters, they said, were sissy stuff, and only mama's boys wrote letters. But I didn't care — there were benefits to writing letters. I knew, because right after I wrote my first letter, I received a goodie box from home. There were even some of Ma's oatmeal-and-date cookies. I figured the reason why some cadets never got goodie boxes was because they never wrote letters.

I had been at the army cadet camp in Vernon, British Columbia, for almost a whole month, and once more it was time to write my weekly letter to the folks back home. Well, actually, my weekly letter was always to Mom. To Mom I could bare my soul. Even though she

119

wasn't sitting right next to me, I could tell her all of my problems. I could relate the smallest problem with the grandest of words. Mom could not only understand those words, but she could interpret each and every one; she instinctively knew what they meant. And her response, although it arrived much later, would always lift my spirits and make me feel good.

My letter continued:

How are the kids? I'm fine. Not much new around here.

Oh yeah, I almost forgot, there is one thing, but it's not new. You know all the stories you hear about army food? Well, you can believe them, Mom. They're true. The cook here has been at it for a month now, and he still hasn't learned a thing about cooking. Everything he cooks tastes the same – that is, everything except for the food in one tub. The cook said it was pickled beets. Now, the pickled beets are really good. You'll have to learn how to make them, Mom. I might be able to teach you when I get home. They should be real easy to make. The cook just slices up a bunch of beets and throws them in a washtub, then he puts water and vinegar over them and calls them pickled beets.

Oh yeah, the army is still teaching us how to drive trucks, and I'm getting real good at it. You can tell Grandfather that when I get home, I'll be trained real well and I'll be ready to drive his old truck. I'll be good enough to haul tamarack fence posts to the prairies, and I can haul the slop from Edson to feed his hogs, in fact, I can even haul his hogs to market. You tell him that I'm ready to drive anytime he wants me.

Oh yeah, Mom, we went on a bivouac this past week. We were gone for two whole days, and I got to drive the truck all the way to Shuswap Lake, and guess what, Mom, I only drove the truck into one tree, but the best part, Mom, was that the army never even found out about it.

Oh, Mom, can you remember to address my mail, particularly my parcels with the cookies, to C/Sgt. Robert Adams. There's another Robert Adams here and he must be getting some of my mail. I saw him eating a cookie that looked a lot like Ma's oatmeal-and-date cookies. When I asked him where he got them, he said it was none of my business, but if it was, he got them from home. But I think he got them from my home. I'm sure they were mine.

Man, I loved to get parcels from home. Especially those with Ma's oatmeal-and-date cookies. They were the yummiest.

I think my sunburn is almost healed now. I lost all the skin off my back, my arms, and my legs. My chest still looks like a pile of ground round, but at least my arms and legs and my back don't burn like they used to.

We walked down to Kalamalka Lake today. I like cutting across the golf course, we're not supposed to, but some of us do. It's much shorter and I always find some golf balls. In fact one rolled right up to me today. When I picked it up, some guy yelled and we all took off running. I think he just wanted to steal the ball I found, but he couldn't run very fast so we got away from him.

For a while I was thinking you shouldn't send me

any more goodie boxes. I don't remember if I told you that I got robbed. Well, I did. And you know what, Mom, it happened right after I got the first goodie box from you.

Man, I remember how excited I was about getting the first parcel from home. I had just gotten back from bivouac and learned I had gotten a parcel from Mom. The War hadn't been over for very long, and I guess Mom hadn't forgotten how the fighting boys enjoyed getting parcels from home. She knew that army mess wasn't all that good and she had baked up a whole bunch of goodies and sent them to me. I tore into that parcel and couldn't believe my eyes as I surveyed all the goodies, especially Ma's homemade oatmeal-and-date cookies. I didn't waste any time in plucking one of those beauties out of the parcel and I gobbled it down as quickly as I could. It was delicious. Then I even shared some of my good fortune with my closest friends. They enjoyed Ma's cookies as much as I did. The rest of my troopmates could only sit around and drool. I'll bet they wished that they had written a letter home.

I decided to save some of the cookies for later. I knew that after eating army chow, I was always still hungry, so what was left of the cookies I put in my barrack box at the end of my bed. Then I went for a stroll down to Polson Park. I liked to poke around in the piles of dead leaves and grass, a haven for salamanders. I dug some up, along with a couple of garter snakes, and then went to check out the fish pond. Over at the pond, I watched a guy thrashing the water to a froth, trying to catch a fish. But the fish weren't interested. I could see them, great big rainbow trout lying in the mossy weeds at the bottom of the pond. If I'd had a willow pole and some snare wire, I'd have shown that guy how to catch fish. I figured I could have caught enough fish to feed the whole camp. It would have given the cook something decent to cook for a change.

Later I returned to barracks. When I walked through the door, I could see little splinters of wood scattered across the floor. My barrack box was no longer at the foot of my bed; it was out in the middle of the aisle. There were so many chips of wood on the floor around the barrack box that it looked as if someone had been splitting firewood. The box looked as if it had been used for artillery practice—the screws popped out of the wood, the hinges busted off and left lying on the floor where they had fallen.

The wrapping from my goodie box was still there, but the goodies were gone. The goodie box was empty. Not even a crumb remained. I was surprised when not a soul in that room had any idea what had happened to my barrack box. No one—not even the friends I had shared my goodies with—had seen a thing. It was like the ghost of the barracks had done it. That night, after I borrowed some tools and fixed my barrack box, I lay on my bunk and I shed a tear for my lost goodies.

The following Saturday I was down at my favourite place, Polson Park, digging through the dead grass and leaves for salamanders. They were something that we didn't have back in Edson, and they fascinated me. I had collected a couple of the more colourful ones when I found a little snake. At first he looked to be all black, but he did have red and yellow stripes on his back. I dropped the salamanders as the snake tried to wriggle away, but I was too quick for him. I caught him, picked him up, and took him back to the barracks with me.

"What have you got there, son?" one of the instructors asked me when I entered the barracks.

"A snake, sir," I replied.

"A snake! Get rid of it," he said, giving me a direct order. "I don't want any snakes around the barracks. Somebody might get bitten."

"But it's only a little snake," I informed him, "and little snakes don't bite, see?" I held it out for him to have a close look. The little snake was twisting and turning in my hand, and as my hand came up the snake swung toward his face. He wasn't too impressed. He recoiled as if he had just been snake-bitten.

"I told you to get rid of that thing before somebody gets hurt!" he bellowed.

"I'll take it back to the park," I said, and walked out of the barracks.

Now, I knew that in the army direct orders are to be followed without question. I knew that to disobey meant I'd be sent home on the next train. But I sorta liked the little guy — it was like he was the only friend I had. Consequently, I didn't take him right back to the park. I decided I would keep him until the next weekend, and then I'd take him back. I carefully slipped him into my pocket, and then later, when I returned to the barracks, I snuck him in and hid him in my barrack box.

At mail call on Monday, I got another goodie box.

This time it was from Ma; she had sent me a whole box of her oatmeal-and-date cookies. I tried to hide Ma's goodie box and sneak it back into the barracks. That was hard to do, however, since every cadet in camp was at mail call, and they all heard my name being called and saw me go up to the front and collect my goodie box.

Back in the room, I plunked myself and the goodie box down on my bunk. I was suddenly very popular, and my so-called friends quickly gathered around, looking for a share of my goodies. But this time I didn't share, for I knew that as soon as I left the room the thieves would strike, and once again my goodies would disappear. While the other guys looked on, I munched away on one cookie after another, trying to eat the whole boxful. That wasn't such a good idea either, because I got sicker than a dog. I was still munching on a cookie when I got the message. I barely had enough time to throw what was left of my goodies into my barrack box, lock it up, and race to the toilets, where I barfed up everything. I thought I was going to die.

When I returned to my bunk, I immediately noticed that it hadn't taken the thief long to strike. For the second time, someone had busted into my barrack box. I knew without looking that all the goodies I hadn't eaten and then barfed up would be gone. The hinges had been broken and the screws had popped out of the wood. The only thing different from the last raid was the lid to my barrack box — this time the lid was still on the box, just a little off-kilter but still there. I knew I was going to have to write and tell the folks not to send any

125

more goodie boxes, that the army had put me up in a den of thieves.

With tears in my eyes and a heavy heart, I lifted the lid and got the surprise of my life. I was shocked to see that all my goodies were still there. Why, the package hadn't even been touched! And there, coiled up right beside my goodie box, was a little black snake with red and yellow stripes running along its back and sides.

"Are you crazy or somethin'?" snarled one of the older cadets. He had been sitting on his bunk watching me. Now he moved closer, not close enough so that he was able to see into my barrack box, but he was sure craning his neck trying to get a peek inside. "Y-you got a snake in that box!"

I quickly slammed the lid shut. I knew for sure that I was in big trouble for not getting rid of the snake, as instructed. There was no doubt in my mind that I would be on the next train home. Now that the lid was closed, the older cadet moved right up to me and stuck his nose in my face. Then other cadets joined him, surrounding me and my barrack box. They weren't scared now — and that's when the light went on in my sometimes dark brain.

"Yeah, I do," I chuckled. "I take it you've seen him. He is a cute little fella, isn't he? Would you like another look?" Then, slowly, I started to lift the lid, and all the cadets quickly moved back.

"Cute? Cute, my butt! Somebody could get bit by that snake. You just better get rid of it, or . . . or else," he snarled.

"Get rid of it? Well, yeah — yeah, I guess I could . . ."

I replied, hesitating before I continued, "but that wouldn't do you no good, 'cause I got more than one snake in there. They're guarding my cookies, and — and oh yeah, guess what?"

"What?" he growled.

"I was up on the hill above the garages — you know, the hill where we're not supposed to go because there's supposed to be rattlesnakes up there. Well, I went up there and — would you believe that there really are rattlesnakes up there, and I actually found one? Yeah, I found a real live rattlesnake!" I said, and then I chuckled as the colour drained from his face, "I — I even caught him, and guess where he's at, right now, this very minute!"

"Y-you . . ." he stammered, struggling to find words. He pointed a finger at my barrack box.

"That's right," I said, "I got a rattlesnake, and he's right here in my barrack box. He's just waiting for the next guy that tries to steal my goodie box, and then he's gonna sink his fangs into those thieving grub hooks."

The look on the older cadet's face was priceless. He was scared silly.

"C'mon, step right up and have a closer look," I said. "You won't be able to see him from back there. You gotta get close, 'cause rattlers like to hide so they can ambush people like you." I smiled as I waved for him to get down and take a closer look. But he was having nothing to do with me or my snakes and he backpedalled away as quickly as he could.

"I-I'm going to report you," he threatened, and his eyes were glued to the barrack box with the busted lid.

"C'mon, don't be a chicken! Come over here. Get closer, and I'll show you," I said, and once more made like I was going to lift the top of the box.

"I'm reporting you!" he declared, and took a couple more steps back.

"Please don't report me," I asked him nicely. "I like my snakes, and if I have to get rid of them, I — well, you know, I might just be forced to let the rattlesnake loose in the bed of the guy who snitched on me."

The space between me and the rest of my troopmates increased as I lifted the lid on my barrack box. I reached in and touched the head of the little garter snake. Suddenly I was hungry again, so I opened the package and took out one of Ma's huge oatmeal-and-date cookies.

I closed the lid on the barrack box. I didn't even bother to lock it. In fact, I didn't bother to replace the screws and the hinges — there was no need. Then I lay back on my army cot and looked up at the ceiling. Yes, I thought to myself, I just might have to climb that hill and check out those rattlesnakes. But first I was going to have to find out what a real rattlesnake looked like.

But don't you worry none, Mom, I figured out how to deal with those thieves all by myself. You can keep sending the goodie boxes, Mom. I'll bet none of those guys will ever break into another barrack box of mine.

Your son,

Bob

A BRICK OF ICE CREAM

Oh, it could get hot on the Stump Farm in early July, and today it was one of those blistering hot summer days, too hot for man or beast to be out in the noonday sun. And here I was, less than a quarter of a mile from home, slaving away in my grandmother's garden, inviting a billion flies to give Grandfather's hogs a rest and turn their attention on me. They swarmed around my head, a black cloud that seemed to travel in never-ending circles. Circles that grew smaller with each passing second as they closed in to suck the remaining juices from my body. I cursed those flies — but I cursed under my breath, to myself, for Ma was also working in the garden and she didn't care much for folks who cursed. And if there was one thing I didn't want to do, it was upset Ma and get sent home early, for I knew there were bound to be some treats at the end of the day. Why, just thinking about it, I could almost taste one of Ma's oatmeal-and-date cookies.

I was crawling around on my hands and knees, pulling weeds from Ma's garden and sweating like a hog. Sweat poured off my brow; it cascaded down my cheeks and dripped off my nose and chin. It was one hot sucker of a day in Ma's garden. Every once in a while, I would pause and wave my arms like crazy, trying to scare the flies back over to Grandfather's hogs. Speaking of hogs, just behind me, in back of the garden, a piglet was squealing like it was being prepared for roasting. I thought about checking on it, but it was too hot to even turn around and see what all the fuss was about. I figured it must be okay, though, for every time the little fellow squealed, an old sow grunted. She could take care of her own.

Mom had sent me down to help Ma in her garden, and I was working my tail off, helping her come to grips with the blanket of weeds that covered her garden. But in the end I knew the hard work would be worth it, for Ma was known to treat those who helped her very well. Actually, whether one was working or not, there was always a treat at Ma's house; but for those who worked hard, there was always a little something special. I wondered what it would be today. Had she baked one of her mouth-watering chocolate cakes, with thick, rich chocolate icing? Or maybe her special doughnuts, sprinkled with sugar and cinnamon? Oh yes, Ma was renowned for her culinary expertise. Many a time, one of my friends would ask if he could accompany me when he learned that I would be stopping at Ma's house. I could only smile as I thought that today I would be in Ma's good books. There were just the two of us on the farm, and I would be her favourite. My mouth watered at the mere thought of what delectable treasure lay at the end of this day's effort. I knew for sure that I would be treated to one of her favourite snacks. Maybe it would be a raisin pie—man, but I loved Ma's raisin pies.

Ma came over to where I was and bent over to inspect my work. My fingers were like a pair of tweezers as I carefully selected each weed to make sure I didn't accidentally grab a vegetable. The weeds were all neatly stacked between the rows of carrots, radishes, beets—weeds lay wilting in the scorching sun, while the green stems of little vegetables stood upright, reaching for the skies.

"That's very good, Bobby," Ma said as she examined the ever-growing pile of weeds. "You didn't even pick one carrot or radish."

"They're too small to eat yet. I'll get them next time, when they're a little bigger," I said, and laughed at my own joke.

"I'm going in now, to make us some lunch," Ma said. "I'll call you when it's ready."

"Oh boy, make lots, Ma. I'm really hungry and thirsty!" I chortled, for this is what I'd been working and waiting for. Finally I was going to get the much-anticipated treat.

It seemed that only a minute had gone by when she called, "Bobby, you can come in and have a bite to eat now!"

"Coming, Ma!" I warbled, jumping to my feet. Instantly I forgot about my sweating brow, the buzzing flies, and the squealing piglet and the grunting sow. I raced across the garden and charged into the house, ready to devour my hard-earned prize.

I stopped short when I looked at the treat that Ma had set out on the table. There was no doubt in my mind that I was feasting my eyes on one of her favourite dishes. She had set out two plates, one for each of us, for there was no way that I was going to get to enjoy this treat all by myself. Ma's plate was at one end of the table, the spot where she always sat. My plate was set at the head of the table, where Grandfather always sat. Today I would get to sit at the head of the table.

On each plate Ma had placed a thick slab of her delicious homemade bread. And then, for reasons known only to her, she had drowned the bread — in fact she had almost buried the whole plate — under a very generous helping of thick cream. I stared in disbelief, for under that sea of white was my slice of bread. I knew it was down there, somewhere, with its rich brown crust, getting soggier by the second. While this was one of Ma's favourite treats, it was far from being one of mine. I almost gagged and I hadn't even had a bite yet. Thankfully, Ma had placed the salt and pepper shakers right beside my plate. I had had this treat before, and I knew from past experience that if I was going to get it down, it needed some doctoring. By the time I finished my plate, it would be black with pepper.

"You shouldn't put so much pepper on your food,

Bobby," Ma scolded me in a good-natured way as I vigorously shook most of the pepper out of the shaker. "That much pepper is not good for you."

"That's the way I like it, Ma," I said, lying through my teeth. I did not want to upset her, for there was still a chance that one of her real good treats could end up on the table.

I looked up and noticed that Ma had almost downed her favourite treat. I took a mouthful, and I gave her a sickly smile and watched as she polished off her lunch. When she had finished, I would have bet that her plate was as clean as it was when it came from the cupboard. I, on the other hand, still had most of my treat left and was struggling, swallowing hard as I tried to down another mouthful. The cream was bad enough—a gooey, sticky mess in my mouth—but this time I think that I might have overdone the pepper. It was something else! And it was making me sweat worse than working in the garden under the noonday sun.

"I-I like my food with lots of pepper, Ma," I said, almost choking on my words.

Just then, without any warning, the door flew open and slammed into the wall behind me. The sudden noise about scared me right out of my wits. I ducked to one side and almost fell right off my chair; in the process I accidentally swallowed the whole mouthful of bread, cream, and of course the black pepper.

"Ma, Ma, I brung you your favourite treat!" warbled my uncle happily as he burst through the door of the farmhouse.

I looked over my shoulder at my uncle. Where had

he come from, I thought, and I quickly looked out the window. I had been so preoccupied with getting the cream and pepper down that I hadn't heard his vehicle drive into the yard. Normally one could hear any vehicle for a country mile. At least I should have heard Nick-the-Dog-Man's dogs. They always barked up a storm at any noise that passed by the front of Nick's place. But there was my uncle's car all right, and here he was, as big as life and grinning like a Cheshire cat as he held out a small brown paper bag for Ma to look at. He was so happy and proud of himself that he almost stumbled over me in his haste to give Ma her favourite treat. I doubt that he even saw me sitting at the table.

I looked at my uncle and then at Ma. Her eyes lit up like the candles on a Christmas tree as she followed the journey of the bag from the door, around the corner of the table, past where I was sitting — before finally stopping just in front of her.

"This is for you. I brung you your favourite treat, Ma," he repeated happily.

"Thank you," Ma replied. She seemed unbelievably calm, but her eyes betrayed her — they were dancing with joy. Ma was excited.

Well now, I can tell you, it didn't take a rocket scientist to know what was in that little brown paper bag. There was only one place I knew that had brown paper bags that size, and when they were shaped like that, it was a given. My uncle had not only brought Ma her favourite treat, he had brought mine as well. I could only sit back and smile at my good fortune. Yes, I thought, as I watched my uncle take an ice-cream brick out of the brown paper bag, good things do come to him who waits. Then I pushed my plate of bread, cream, and black pepper to one side—it could wait. Right now there was better cream to be had. Ice cream.

I watched the man who right at that moment was certainly my favourite uncle, as he carefully peeled away the wrapper, a cardboard wrapper that kept the treat in that perfect shape, a rectangle the same size as a pound of butter. There on the table before us was a treat that every little boy or girl, or for that matter any grandmother, would die for on such a hot summer day. Three flavours of ice cream—chocolate, vanilla, and best of all, strawberry. Had I not been afraid of losing sight of the prize, I'm certain that I could have closed my eyes and savoured each flavour. My taste buds were really working overtime now, as I watched that brick of Neapolitan ice cream. I never said a word; I just waited patiently for my share.

"Thank you," Ma said again, and her voice echoed the happiness that was in her eyes.

"I brung it just for you, Ma," warbled my uncle again.

"Then I guess we'd better have some right now, before it melts," Ma declared. "Bobby is here too. He's helping me in the garden."

"Oh ya," replied my uncle, ignoring me.

Ma started to get up from her chair, but my uncle reached over and gently pushed her back.

"You stay sitting, Ma," said my uncle. "I'll serve. This is my treat. I brung it special, just for you."

I sat there in silence, hardly able to believe my good

135

luck. I knew that brick of ice cream had to be eaten then and there, for on the farm there was no way to keep it from melting. Even the well, where we kept such things as butter and milk and even meat, wouldn't prevent ice cream from melting. No, here I was, looking at a whole brick of ice cream that had to be eaten. Normally, whenever a brick of ice cream appeared on the farm — and that wasn't too often — a horde of people also appeared, and a person was lucky to get even a teaspoon of it. No, I couldn't believe my good luck: today there were only the three of us there to do the deed.

My uncle strode over to the cupboard and took out one plate, then he grabbed Ma's big butcher knife and a handful of spoons. I wanted to shout at him that he only needed three spoons and that by bringing more, he would bring us bad luck — more spoons meant that others would arrive and we'd have to share our ice cream. I didn't relish the thought of sharing my third of the brick of ice cream. But I held my tongue.

Clutching the knife in one hand, my uncle paused for a second and held it up to eye level; he smiled at the knife, then at Ma, before returning to the table. I was all eyes as he dropped the spoons on the table before laying the business edge of the knife on top of that brick.

Again I wanted to shout: Don't forget there's three of us here! Once more I held my tongue. My heart just about stopped beating when he cut the first slice off — half of the brick of ice cream was in that first slice. But that was okay. I watched as he dropped it onto Ma's plate, the one she had just wiped clean. I had been hoping that I might get a third of that brick, but I consoled myself. Like he said, he had, after all, brought that treat just for Ma. I would be more than happy with a quarter of the brick.

"Eat up, Ma," he said. My uncle was standing—no, hovering—over Ma, and he gave a funny little laugh, more like a giggle. "C'mon, Ma! Eat up, now. I brung this just for you."

Ma didn't need a second invite. Anyway, on such a hot day, there was no sense letting good ice cream melt. My uncle and I both watched as she picked up her spoon and virtually attacked that half-brick of ice cream.

"Ain't it good, Ma?" asked my uncle, as he waited to be congratulated on his thoughtfulness. "Ain't it good? I brung it just for you!"

"It's good!" Ma replied, almost mumbling between mouthfuls.

There was one thing for sure, Ma's portion of ice cream was not going to melt before she devoured it. My uncle stood back with a silly grin on his face and watched Ma, but not me—I turned my attention to the remaining half-brick of ice cream. I could see the corners of my share beginning to sag as they surrendered to the heat. My share of the brick was melting away before my eyes. I desperately wanted to bring this to my uncle's attention, but he was so engrossed in watching Ma enjoy her ice cream that a word from me just then might have compromised my share. My lips were sealed.

Ma finished her ice cream and was carefully scraping up the last of what had melted. She had sure enjoyed her share; I was dying waiting for mine. Finally my uncle, still smiling, took the knife to the remaining half-brick of ice cream. I was delighted when he cut it in half: one-quarter of a brick for him, and one-quarter of a brick for me. Then he paused, slowly turned, and looked at me. It was the first time that he had acknowledged my existence. The smile faded from his face.

"You haven't finished eating your lunch yet," he said. "Your plate is still covered with cream and — and all that . . . that . . ." and a look of disgust crossed his face. "What is that black junk?"

"Pepper, and I'm eating it!" I replied. I quickly grabbed for my plate, shovelled a huge helping of bread, cream, and pepper into my mouth, and gulped it down.

At this point, my uncle scraped his portion of the ice cream onto his plate, then plunked his butt onto a chair and picked a spoon off the pile. The smile returned to his face as he shovelled in a huge helping of his ice cream.

"Wasn't it good, Ma?" he asked between spoonfuls. All the while, I was shoveling homemade bread, thick cream, and tons of black pepper into my mouth. "I brung you your favourite treat, didn't I?"

"You sure did," Ma replied, and she sat back with a satisfied smile on her face.

A quick glance at my portion of the ice cream told me that it was rapidly succumbing to the heat. It was beginning to spread across the cardboard wrapper. In a panic, I buried my head in my plate. There was no doubt that time was a critical factor; I had to clean up my plate as quickly as possible. I could only thank my lucky stars that by now the cream had completely destroyed the bread, rendering it a soggy mess. Even though I felt like throwing up with every mouthful, I was able to spoon it into my mouth and swallow it all in one motion.

When I finally choked down the last of the bread, cream, and pepper, I reached for my share of the ice cream. But I stopped short — my share of the ice cream was gone. Not only was my share of the ice cream gone, but so was the cardboard wrapper. I looked at my uncle and could hardly believe what I saw. My uncle had that wrapper, and he was holding it up to his face and licking what was left on it with his big fat tongue. He was sitting there smiling, and licking the cardboard like a dog.

"I brung it for you, Ma, and — and for me," he said between licks.

I watched, stunned, as he licked that cardboard wrapper as clean as a whistle. There was no ice cream for little Bobby Adams on this hot summer day.

A few minutes later, I was back in the garden. The swarm of flies had not deserted me; they were waiting just outside the door. They followed me back to the garden and picked up where they left off. Under the blazing noonday sun, flies buzzed around my head like crazy. Back by the barn, that stupid piglet was still squealing its fool head off, and the old sow was still grunting. Down on my hands and knees, I thought I was going to puke. I had terrible indigestion, and every time I burped I got a foul taste in my mouth. It was the taste of bread, black pepper, and cream that was now sour beyond all belief. I was sweating madly as I savagely attacked the weeds. I yanked weeds out by the handfuls, along with little carrots, radishes, and beets that were way too small to eat.

FREE HAY

The clear sky and hot morning sun brought the promise of a perfect August day for swimming in the McLeod River. Chores had been rushed through, and we four Adams children quickly changed our work clothes for bathing suits before sitting down to breakfast. The weather had been brutally hot for the past week, and we were all anticipating a refreshing plunge—actually it was more like a splashing around the shallow shoreline, for none of us could swim—in the icy waters of the McLeod River.

I was just finishing my breakfast when Grandfather suddenly burst through the door. "I could sure use your help today, Boy!"

Those were the first words out of his mouth, and Grandfather said them to me, but he was looking at Mom. As he plunked himself down at the table, he didn't even notice (or if he did, he ignored the fact) that we were all sitting around it in our bathing suits.

"We're all going swimming today," I told him. Normally I would have done anything to be the one who was asked to help Grandfather. But in this weather not even the privilege of working with Grandfather could match the lure of the cool freshness of the river waters.

"Give me a cuppa that coffee, Girl," Grandfather said, ignoring my comment. "Old Hubert says he isn't goin' to be able to take his hay off this year, and he said if I wanted it, I could have it. All I gotta do is put it up."

"We're going swimming," I said again, just in case he hadn't heard me the first time. After all, Grandfather wasn't getting any younger. In fact I had heard Ma say that she noticed he had selective hearing, whatever that was.

"Hubert said he even had a tractor there that we could use," Grandfather said to no one in particular, but I knew who he was talking to. "I'd say that whoever helped me just might get a chance to drive that tractor. All we have to do is get it started."

"I don't want to drive that dumb old tractor," I said. I had been to old Hubert's place before and I had seen his tractor. "It's nothing but a piece of junk."

"Bobby, you get dressed and go help your grandfather," Mom said.

"But, Mom—" I started to protest, but she cut me short.

"Get dressed and go help your Grandfather," Mom said in her no-nonsense voice. "You can always go swimming tomorrow."

"It shouldn't take us more'n a week, Boy,"

Grandfather said, and he took a big slurp of his coffee. Then he added, "That's if we can get that tractor started."

"A-a week!" I said, not believing what I had just heard. "But Mom, th-that means I-I won't get to go swimming for a whole week."

"Get changed," Mom said. "I'm sure that river will still be there when you're finished."

With heavy heart, I got back into my work clothes and followed Grandfather out the door for what I knew would be a hot, sticky week in old Hubert's hayfield. I think it was the first time in my life that I did not want to be the one chosen to help Grandfather.

"You . . . you brought horses! Where's your truck?" I asked Grandfather before we even got around to the back of the house. I couldn't see the horses, but I knew they were there. I could hear the hum of the flies that swarmed around them in this heat before I even came to the corner of the house.

"I sure did, Boy," Grandfather replied happily. "This job calls for horses, not trucks."

"Where'd you get those horses?" I asked as I turned the corner at the back of the house. There was a cloud of flies buzzing over the team, a blanket of flies that almost covered the horses. There were flies of every size and description—houseflies, big bluebottle flies, manure flies, horseflies, and deer flies. The only parts of those horses that gave any indication that either one of them was alive were their tails, which were swishing around like propellers in a vain effort to keep a good portion of the flies airborne.

143

"They belong to old Hubert," Grandfather replied. "I went over to his place and picked them up this morning. Old Hubert has a good crop of hay this year, and we're going to need his horses and the hayrack to bring a load home tonight."

"Tonight!" I said. "You mean we're going to haul hay tonight too?"

"We will if you quit talking so's we can get goin'," Grandfather declared.

Old Hubert's team, or rather old Hubert's nags, were so pitiful-looking it was a wonder they could stand, let alone walk and pull a wagon. The nags were hooked up to Grandfather's hay wagon and tied up in the trees behind the house. They were in the shade, out of the burning sun, but they could not escape the flies. Flies swarmed in clouds around the two old nags. It was hard to say whether it was the trees or the flies that were holding those old horses up.

We hadn't even started, and already I was dreading this day.

"It's a good thing old Hubert had this team," Grandfather said. "We'll hafta use them till we get the tractor goin' — that is, if we can get 'er goin'. Old Hubert said he ain't had it runnin' in a while now."

Oh yeah, great, I thought, a team of horses and a tractor. Suddenly I had a real good idea of who would be driving the horses and who would be driving that old tractor — if we got it going.

Grandfather and I climbed up into the hayrack. As those old nags plodded out of the yard, I figured that at least half of those flies discovered that Grandfather and

I didn't have tails to shoo them away. Grandfather drove and I stood beside him, flapping my arms like crazy at the cloud of flies all the way to old Hubert's hayfield — four long, miserable miles. It took forever, and the sun got hotter and hotter with each passing minute. I hadn't even started to work, and already I was sweating.

"Somebody's already cut your hay, Grandfather," I said, noting that some of the hay was already lying on the ground.

"Old Hubert cut some of it," Grandfather replied, "but he said I could have what he cut, as well."

Then we both turned our attention to the tractor. Old Hubert said that the tractor had died a couple of years back and he hadn't been able to get it working. To say that it didn't work, or that it had cut its last round of hay, was an understatement. Hubert was right, I thought, the tractor was dead — he just hadn't bothered to bury it. But Grandfather had different thoughts.

"I think the old girl looks pretty good," Grandfather said as he slowly walked around the tractor, giving it his critical eye. "What do you think, Boy?"

"I think if I was you, Grandfather, I'd put all my effort into those horses while they're still standing," I replied, giving my honest opinion. But Grandfather ignored my advice. He was bent on getting that old tractor started. Grandfather seemed to have the idea that if he didn't get the tractor started, he was not going to get that free hay.

"Let's see if we can tell what's wrong. Give that crank a spin, Boy," Grandfather said.

Grudgingly, I grabbed onto the crank that was sticking out of the front of the engine and gave it a spin, as Grandfather directed. I cursed under my breath when nothing happened, because it didn't spin—in fact it was all I could do to make it turn. I spat on my hand to get a better grip and was getting ready to take another stab at it.

"Hold yer horses a minute there, Boy," Grandfather said, and he put his head in under the hood as close to the engine as he could get. I noticed that his tongue was wedged firmly into the corner of his mouth.

Grandfather was in his glory—he loved to tinker with engines. He tinkered and he sweated. Mom always said that nobody knew motors better than Grandfather, that all he had to do was put his hand on the hood and he could tell what was wrong. Grandfather talked to that old tractor like it was a baby. And every so often, he'd call to me when he felt he had softened her up.

"Give 'er another spin, Boy," he'd warble.

Once more, with great anticipation and with sweat streaming off my face, I would spit on my hand, which had already turned red from the rust, grab hold of the old crank with my hand, and turn it with all my might. When we started, I can honestly say that I had all the faith in the world in Grandfather—I knew that if anyone could get that old tractor running, it would be Grandfather. But now I was starting to have my doubts.

"Maybe we should use those horses before they fall over," I said to Grandfather. "This pile of scrap should have been dumped over the side of a cliff a long time ago."

"Don't you worry none, Boy," Grandfather said. "There's a lot of good miles left in this old girl yet."

"You could have fooled me," I mumbled to myself.

Grandfather didn't give up. He tinkered and talked, and I spun the crank, and I sweated and cursed under the scorching August sun. And then, as if miracles never cease, there was a sign of life in the old girl. A pitiful little cough escaped from the engine, and a belch of black smoke rose from the smokestack. I couldn't believe my ears and eyes. I cursed myself for ever doubting Grandfather's abilities to coax life out of a motor.

"We did it, Grandfather!" I cried. "We did it!"

The old tractor shuddered, and then, as the smoke rose slowly into the blue sky — it died again. All was silent, except for the humming of the flies, which sounded like a roar, a constant vibration in my ears.

"Spin 'er again, Boy!" Grandfather hollered, for the weak cough was the sign he had worked for, and he was not about to lose the old girl. "Spin 'er again!"

And spin her again I did. With renewed vigour and hope, I put all my strength into turning that old crank. Nothing happened.

"Again!" yelled Grandfather excitedly, and I spun that darned old crank again, although not nearly as hard as the time before. Nothing again.

"Once more!" Grandfather yelled. "I think we've got 'er now."

"I think I've about had it," I complained as I half-heartedly leaned into the crank one more time. This time I got the surprise of my life.

Once more the old engine coughed. Then there was a loud POP and the world I was standing in suddenly flipped upside down. I found myself lying on the ground. My whole arm was numb. I thought for a minute that the engine had sprung to life, but no such luck. It was a backfire.

"Yeow!" I howled. That crank had kicked back so fast that I was spun to the ground and the crank was torn from my hand.

"Are you okay, Boy?" Grandfather asked, hustling around to the front of the tractor, where I lay screaming and clutching my arm.

"My arm's broken!" I wailed as I rolled around on the ground. "You and your stupid tractor broke my arm! Now I can't go swimming!"

"Here, Boy, let me see," Grandfather said, kneeling over me.

"Don't touch me! You broke my arm and it hurts!" I howled. I pulled my arm away from him.

"You're movin' your arm, Boy," Grandfather said. "It's not broken."

"It's not?" I stopped howling long enough to take a good look at my throbbing arm.

"Of course it's not broken," Grandfather said. "You wouldn't be able to move it if it was broke. Now, quit layin' around here and howlin' like a baby. Get back on that crank and give 'er another spin. I think we've got 'er now, Boy."

As usual, Grandfather was right. My arm was sore but it wasn't broken, and on the very next spin of the crank, the old tractor barked, coughed once, and then roared to life. Even the old nags lifted their heads and looked on in amazement. Grandfather had done the impossible.

I helped him as he hooked the hay mower on behind the tractor, and then he surveyed the rusty old horse-drawn dump hay rake that lay almost hidden in high grass and Russian thistle. To the rake he hooked the horses and the swarm of flies. Standing to one side of the rake, he called the horses to action.

"Giddy-up!" he sang out as he slapped the reins across their butts.

That old rake had been sitting for some time, and the grass and thistle were wrapped tightly around the metal wheels. There was a lot of snorting and blowing from both ends of those poor old nags as they threw their weight into the task. A terrible screeching noise pierced the countryside and drowned all other sounds as the wheels grudgingly pulled free of their bonds. The old dump hay rake rolled out into the hayfield. Except for needing a healthy shot of axle grease, the rake appeared to be in much better shape than the tractor. Grandfather climbed onto the rake, settled his butt onto the rusty metal seat, and pulled the lever to raise the rake. It, too, squeaked like crazy, but the rake lifted high off the ground and settled behind the seat. There was no doubt that the old rake was rusty, from the tines to the tongue hitch, but all the parts seemed to work. Then, to my amazement, Grandfather called to the horses.

"Giddy-up!" he said, and his voice had a triumphant ring.

Grandfather was in a good mood as the horses,

under their swarm of flies, slowly moved into the mowed field. I forgot about my sore arm as I climbed onto the tractor and watched him make a complete circuit of the field. The horses moved slowly, and when a certain amount of hay had been collected, Grandfather would trip the gear and the rake tines would rise up, dropping their load of hay in a pile. Then the tines would drop back to the ground to collect more hay. This was repeated all the way around the field.

"Okay, Boy, don't just sit there, let's get goin' and make some hay while the sun shines," Grandfather said when he returned.

"You bet!" I replied. I was going to drive the tractor, and now for the first time I was really ready to help. "How do I get this thing in gear, Grandfather?"

"No no, Boy, not the tractor. C'mon over here," Grandfather said. "You take the horses."

"B-but . . . y-you said—"

"I said, you take the horses, Boy. I gotta make sure that tractor is running properly. Now, do you know how to run this rake?"

"Yeah," I muttered. "I know how to run that thing."

"You remember, Boy, when that rake gets full, you make sure you dump all the hay right where I did. I don't want to have to run all over the field to pick it up."

I watched Grandfather and the tractor over in the far field. They appeared to be zipping around the field, making round after round. Grandfather was giving that tractor a good workout while he made sure it was working. Meanwhile, the horses and the flies and I had only made a couple of rounds with the rake. As the hot sun got hotter the horses moved more slowly, and their heads were drooping so low they were almost touching the ground. The swarm of flies never stopped — in fact it seemed to me that several thousand more had just joined the party.

Suddenly one of those old horses snorted, and his head shot up high into the air. His ears perked up and he snorted again. Then the second horse also came to life; it snorted and jumped. About that time, one of those flies ignored my incessant swatting and attacked my neck with a hot foot, nailing me with a vicious, searing pain. Before I knew what was happening, I got a second shot. Both horses bolted.

This sudden burst of activity and jolt of energy caught me by complete surprise. I had been favouring my arm, the one that had been cranked when the tractor backfired. Except for swatting at the flies with my good arm, I had been lulled into a false sense of security. I had been quite relaxed as I sat on the rusty metal seat of that old hay rake. If I hadn't been swatting at flies, I probably would have fallen asleep. I wasn't paying much attention to the slow plodding of the old horses, and even less attention to the reins.

When the horses took off, so did I, and so did the reins. The rusty seat shot forward, and the reins were jerked from my hands. I made a frantic stab to get the reins back, but to no avail — they and the horses were gone. As the rake jerked and bounced forward, following the rapidly departing horses, the rusty seat shot out from under me. My feet shot up as I started to float backwards up and over the seat. In desperation, I shot my good arm forward, grabbing for anything to regain my balance. I was lucky when my hand found the front of that rusty old seat. I held on for dear life. Suddenly one of the metal wheels hit a rock, and the rake took a wild bounce. I flew into the air, and when I came down my butt slammed into the back of the seat.

Then I heard another noise. Amidst all the chaos, it was very clear and distinct.

PING

I knew immediately what it was—it was the sickening sound of the lone rusty old bolt that held the metal seat to the rake. The stress of my butt slamming down onto the seat was too much for that bolt. It snapped. Once more I was airborne, but this time I had the seat for company. My legs sailed up high into the air as both the seat and I parted company with the rake. I had a sense of floating as I tumbled head over heels. I remember hitting the long tines of the rake—it was like landing on a spring, and I bounced high into the air. While I was in the air, I realized that the buzzing had become frantic as the flies swarmed around my head. When I came down the second time, the rake was gone, and there was only the hard, sun-baked ground to greet me. I slammed into the ground. This time I did not bounce, and the wind was knocked out of me.

As I lay there, gasping to get my breath, I realized that half that swarm of flies had not left with the horses. And those hummers that stayed were not flies. They were yellow jackets, and they were mad. I knew instantly that I had raked up a wasps' nest, and the horses and I were paying dearly for it. Heading for a grove of poplar trees, the poor old nags went stampeding off across the field, the rake bouncing crazily after them. As for me, I forgot about my arm, and trying to catch my breath as I leapt to my feet, I charged away in the other direction flailing my arms wildly. I was headed straight for the only protection that I knew of—Grandfather.

Grandfather saw me coming. He leapt off the tractor and he raced across the field to meet me. I was surprised that he could run that fast. Well . . . that is, he was running towards me until he saw what I was bringing to him. Then he turned and headed for the poplar trees too, and I realized that he could run even faster.

*   *   *

"I'm going swimming tomorrow," I told Mom when I got home. She looked at me curiously and examined the dabs of mud that adorned my face, neck, and arms.

"I thought we had agreed that you'd be helping Grandfather until he got the hay put up."

"He said he doesn't need my kind of help," I replied.

"He doesn't? Why not?" Mom asked.

"I don't think he was too happy with me," I replied. "All the way home he kept mumbling about me breaking old Hubert's hay rake, and it's gonna cost him more to fix the rake than the hay's worth—and he said something about how there's no such thing as free hay."

153

AN UNLIKELY COUPLE

For as far back as I can remember, John and Veona Ernst, my maternal grandparents, were never much farther than a stone's throw away. When we lived in Wildwood, they lived just down the block. When we moved to Hornbeck, they also moved to Hornbeck. And when we finally settled on the Stump Farm—well, they were on the farm just to the north of us, less than a quarter of a mile away. I spent a considerable amount of my early years with my grandparents. I was very close to both of them and, as is reflected in my stories, they had a huge influence on my life.

Ma and Grandfather, as they were called by absolutely everybody who knew them, could very easily have been the original Odd Couple, so different were they in their beliefs and habits—as different as night and day. But they got along beautifully, and I doubt that there was ever a harsh word passed between them. The fact that these two people, so different in every way, would even come to the point of courting each other, let alone wed, was something of a miracle. It was, shall we say, the perfect mismatch.

Ma was a very religious person, and her faith in the Lord and in her church was unshakeable. Her whole life was dedicated to the church and the Bible, with one exception—Grandfather always came first.

Grandfather was another story. He was not the least bit religious, and I seriously doubt if he ever saw the inside of a church. He never went to church, but he was always there to take Ma, and then to pick her up. He made sure that she never missed a church meeting or gathering.

Ma's religion forbade playing cards. She never even permitted a pack of playing cards in her house. In fact, I do not ever recall Ma being in a house where cards were being played, for playing cards was a sin. Grandfather, on the other hand, loved to play cards, and play cards he did whenever the opportunity arose—but it was always at someone else's house. Often it was a rousing game of whist at the Stump Farm, and nothing gave him more pleasure than to trump a mighty ace with a lowly deuce.

Ma's religion also forbade drinking, and to my grandmother even a soda pop was taboo. The strongest drink that she ever had was a cup of hot water spiked with a small shot—of milk. Yes, water, juice, and milk were the only drinks that she permitted herself. Anything else was a no-no, and alcohol was strictly taboo. Alcohol, like cards, was never allowed in her house. "It is the drink of the devil himself," I had often heard her say.

Grandfather, on the other hand, was never far from the drink he loved. "Just a snort, Boy, just a snort," he would say as he tipped the bottle. Rye whisky was his drink of choice.

Grandfather's drink could never be found in Ma's house. He did, however, have it stashed in various places around the farm — in his truck, in the garage, in an old boot, in the manger, or in a nest box in the chicken coop. Yes, Grandfather's drink could be found anyplace where a mickey could be concealed. Grandfather loved his rye whisky.

Ma's religion also forbade the eating of pork or any pork products. "Pigs are filthy animals. They are dirty and not fit for human consumption," she would often say. But therein lay a problem, because grandfather was a farmer; and in particular, he was a pig farmer. His farm could be home to several hundred pigs at any given time. Not only did he raise pigs, but he loved his eggs with bacon or ham for breakfast, and he loved side ribs, pork chops, and pork roasts. I don't think there was a part of the pig that Grandfather didn't like.

Grandfather ate pork often, and it was Ma who prepared it for him. Now, Ma was a fabulous cook, and she did an excellent job on every meal, whether it was bacon and eggs, a ham, strudel, pot roast, bread, or fancy dessert. However, cooking meals for Grandfather that included pork in any form was very traumatic for Ma. Whenever she cooked that forbidden product, she would pray to the good Lord not to strike her dead for this horrible sin she was committing. And cooking pork products and putting them on the table for Grandfather was as far as she ever went—never did she even taste one tiny morsel.

Ma never voiced an opinion on politics; but Grandfather did, and he was very outspoken. However, on election day they both went to the polls. Everyone knew how Grandfather would vote, and he was not shy about telling Ma how she should vote. But Ma was her own person, and if you asked who she had voted for, she would tell you without any hesitation. She voted for the other guy, whoever Grandfather wasn't voting for, because nobody, not even Grandfather, could tell her how to vote. She was quite happy just being able to cancel Grandfather's vote.

My grandmother was a homemaker, a job she took seriously and did very well. And Grandfather—well, Grandfather was a rounder, a gregarious, fun-loving rascal who always seemed to have a smile on his face. How these two people ever got together, I'll never know. But for two people who were so completely different, I must say that I never heard either one raise their voice in anger to the other. They were the most mismatched perfect couple I have ever known.

I'm grateful for all the time I spent with them in my youth, but like many rural Albertans of the time, I was destined to move on, and eventually I left the Stump Farm and Ma and Grandfather behind. As is inevitable, distance dictated that I saw less and less of my grandparents. They were always so young and full of life, but it seemed they grew old in my absence. One of the last times I saw my Grandfather alive was when he and Ma visited my family in Calgary. He was an old man, and yet he still embodied everything I remembered.

*   *   *

"Just a minute, Grandfather, and I'll give you a hand as soon as I help Ma into the house," I said as the old man struggled to get out from behind the steering wheel of his Buick.

"Boy, I've been getting in and out of cars all my life, and I'm not that old that I need your help today," he grumbled, as if my making the offer was the ultimate insult. "It just takes me a little longer now, that's all. You go on ahead and help Ma. I'll be fine."

My grandparents, both in their seventies, had stopped by for an unexpected visit. Being a helpful grandchild and a good host, I was attempting to help them get from their car into the house.

With Ma out of the car, I watched as Grandfather painfully moved first one foot out from behind the steering wheel, where it dropped to the ground. Dead weight if there ever was any, I thought. Then the second foot moved; that was obviously even more painful than the first move. He moaned and groaned the whole time, as if he was about ready to die. I wanted to offer to help him again, but held back. No sense insulting him twice within the first five minutes of their visit, I thought.

I guided Ma up the sidewalk. She was not too proud to accept an arm, and she clung to me like glue. Grandfather walked — or more truthfully he shuffled along — ahead of us. Watching him move so carefully, unable to lift his feet, I was glad that I had washed the hopscotch lines off the cement. In his condition he most certainly would have tripped over one of them.

The problem probably stemmed from Grandfather's back. I could tell that it was bothering him. He was bent forward, his right hand held tightly on his hip. His hand obviously provided the support necessary to keep him from falling forward and landing flat on his nose. He stopped for a rest about halfway between the car and the house.

"I tell you," he moaned loud enough for half the city to hear, "it's hell to get old, Boy. Hell to get old. Yer bones is sore all the time."

"You just wait there for a minute, Grandfather," I told him, ignoring the fact that I was precariously close to insulting him again. "I'll take Ma into the house and come back for you."

He started shaking his head. "Boy, I can get into the house by myself," he snorted indignantly. "I ain't dead yet."

On up the sidewalk he shuffled, his hand still holding his hip in place. I figured that the step would pose too great an obstacle, as it lacked a handrail; however, it proved to be nothing that a few loud moans, groans, and a good grunt couldn't overcome.

Grandfather scaled the two steps to the door and shuffled off into the living room.

It was fortunate that we had the chesterfield strategically located in the room, for Grandfather had expended all his energy by the time he reached it. Not having the strength left in his old body to lower himself, he uttered another loud moan and literally collapsed onto the seat. The sudden stop on the soft cushion must have hurt his bones and joints immensely, for he let out a sharp "AAAEEEYYYYIIII" which he followed up with a chorus of groans. Everyone in the neighbourhood was now aware that Grandfather had landed.

"Are you hungry, or thirsty?" Mar asked my grandparents once they were both comfortably seated.

"Nothing for me, Girl," Grandfather responded immediately between groans. "I just want to sit for a minute. I'll be okay in a minute or two."

"That would be nice. I'll have a cup of hot water," Ma replied, "and just a little milk."

"One cup of hot water and a shot of milk, coming right up!" I repeated the order to make sure that it was right. "Are you sure you don't want anything to drink, Grandfather?" I asked, confirming Grandfather's earlier decision by force of habit, since he had been known to change his mind on very short notice.

"No, Boy. I just want to sit for a minute. I'll be fine," he moaned.

Mar was in the kitchen getting Ma's hot water, complete with a shot of milk, when Grandfather began to stir. It was a painful experience that he was inflicting on his old body, and it was made even more noticeable

160

by the contortions of his face. His tongue was sticking out the side of his mouth, wedged firmly between his lips as he placed one hand on the armrest of the chesterfield and pushed the other deep into the cushion in the process of struggling to get to his feet.

"Can I help you, Grandfather?" I asked, trying to be polite and helpful, although I knew what the answer would be.

"I can get out of my car by myself and I can get up from the chesterfield by myself," he snorted.

However, the chesterfield was proving to be a far greater challenge than the driver's seat of the Buick. Grandfather was having a devil of a time with that soft, spongy cushion of the chesterfield. He found himself a little off-kilter as he fought to rise from his seat. All eyes were on him as he moaned and groaned himself to a standing position. He shuffled towards the kitchen, and I followed. One can never be too cautious, I told myself, pussyfooting along behind him. I didn't really want him to know that I was there, but I wanted to be close enough to catch him should he suddenly collapse in a heap on the floor.

Once in the kitchen, he shuffled straight over to Mar.

"Girl," he said, and he spoke very quietly. It was the first time he had uttered a sound that could not be heard for blocks. "Girl, you wouldn't happen to have just a little shot of whisky, would you?" he asked, with a pained look on his old face.

"Just for you, Grandfather," Mar said, and smiled at him. "I think I know where I can find one, just for you."

"That's good!" He smiled for the first time.

"You go back in and sit down," Mar told him, "and I'll bring it right in."

"No! No, Girl!" he said in a whisper, and one could hear the urgency in his voice. "Not in there, Girl. Ma's in there. Just put a stiff drink in a glass, and set it in the bathroom."

Yes, Mar would have committed the cardinal sin by bringing a drink of whisky into a room where Grandmother was — Grandmother, who neither drank nor approved of drinking. Grandfather had spent his whole life having a quick drink — and there had been many — out of sight of Grandmother.

"You want me to put a glass of whisky in the bathroom for you?" Mar asked, looking a little surprised at the odd request.

"Shush — shush, girl, not so loud. Ma will hear you," he cautioned Mar. Then he quickly glanced over his shoulder towards the door. He was relieved to see that I was the only one there and he gave me a sly wink.

"Okay," Mar whispered, "I'll put the glass in the bathroom."

"Good girl," he whispered, and sighed with relief. A huge grin crossed his face as he turned and slowly shuffled out the door. Back in the living room, there was another piercing shriek as he dropped to the chesterfield, where he moaned until the latest round of aches subsided.

Mar brought Ma her cup of hot water spiked with just the right amount of milk. With Ma busy sipping her drink, Mar returned to the kitchen and poured a very healthy shot of rye into a large tumbler and walked it into the bathroom. When she returned to the room and sat down, Grandfather gave her a big smile and a wink. Then he went through the painful effort to once again extract himself from the sofa.

I would have bet that he wouldn't make the bathroom. Several times I thought that he was going to fall before he reached the door, but miraculously he managed to regain his balance. There was little doubt that my Grandfather was getting old. He was aging quickly, showing the toll that years of hard labour had exacted, but he was a gutsy old guy. I had to marvel at his stamina as he disappeared through the door.

It seemed that Grandfather had not been in the bathroom for ten seconds when the door suddenly flew open. Out through the door he came, and there was a smile a mile wide on his old face. He came back into the room as frisky as a young colt. Into the centre of the room he pranced. Then suddenly, without warning, with all eyes upon him, Grandfather leapt high into the air and clicked his heels together. He was as graceful as a Russian dancer as he landed effortlessly on the floor. Cutting a fine pirouette on the rug, he turned and nimbly stepped over to the chesterfield, then gracefully lowered himself onto the soft cushion.

Gone were the aches. Gone were the pains. Gone was the moaning. Gone was the groaning. Grandfather was suddenly full of life, and he lit up the room with conversation and his unique brand of storytelling. When he wasn't laughing and joking, he sat on the sofa with the biggest, most satisfied grin on his face.

This is how I choose to remember my grandfather. A rounder to the end. Every day a new adventure. Telling stories and singing his song. He lived life to the fullest.

*   *   *

After my grandfather passed away, Ma was on her own. She relied on her family and friends and got even more involved in her church.

I was always happy to help her out, but since I lived such a distance away my opportunities were limited. I was pleased when I got the opportunity to take Ma to an eye specialist in Calgary; Ma was staying with my uncle across the city.

"My appointment's for eight-thirty tomorrow morning," Ma said, "but I don't have a ride."

"That's okay, Ma. I'll take you," I said.

"Bobby, are you sure it's no bother to take me? I don't want to be a bother."

"Ma, I can assure you, you're no bother. I'd love to take you. I'll just call the office and let them know that I'll be in around ten."

"It won't take long, Bobby. The doctor's from the church, you know, and I used to go to school with his mother. She was my best friend in school, you know, Bobby. When the minister from the church made the appointment for me, he said it would only take a half an hour."

I'm sure that Ma could have gone to an eye doctor in Edson or Edmonton and avoided the long trip to

Calgary, but the specialist that she had come to see was the person she knew not only could, but would fix her eyes. For this was not just any specialist. This specialist, this person she had travelled more than three hundred miles to see, was also a person of her faith. In fact, for my grandmother it got even better than that, for she had gone to school with the specialist's mother. As young girls, they had been the best of friends. Why, this visit would be like going to visit an old family friend. Once Ma learned that this specialist existed, he was the only person in the world Ma would trust her failing eyes to. I had never met this man, and neither had Ma, but if ever there was a miracle worker, this was the person.

How could anyone doubt this man's healing abilities? I know, after listening to my dear old grandmother, I too shared the happiness she felt, and it was easy to get caught up in her enthusiasm as she talked about this wonderful specialist. She was indeed fortunate to have made this discovery in her hour of need. I could hardly wait to meet this miracle worker, for after listening to Ma, I myself was ready to run down and have my glasses checked.

To say that Ma was elated when we arrived at the optometrist's office shortly before eight the next morning would be an understatement. She was as happy as a schoolgirl going to her first prom as we stood and waited at the locked door. We were there for about half an hour — to me it felt as though we had been there all morning — before a couple of young women arrived. One of them produced a key and opened the office. Neither of them paid any attention to the elderly lady escorted by a Fish Cop in full uniform.

Ma walked in behind them, and I followed. I couldn't help but notice that there was a bit of a spring in Ma's legs as she strode, as well as an elderly lady can stride, up to the receptionist's desk. Ma was just as proud as a peacock. I quickly forgot about the wait, and a tear welled up in my eye as I felt a little tug on the old heartstrings. I would have taken the whole day off just to be part of an experience that gave my grandmother such great pleasure.

"I'm Mrs. Ernst," Ma announced proudly to the receptionist.

"Have a seat, Mrs. Ernest. We'll call you in a few minutes," came the cool, clinical response.

"That's 'Ernst'," I corrected her, and I spelled it out so that she would be sure to get it correct the next time.

"I used to go to school with the doctor's mother," Ma informed the receptionist proudly.

"That's nice," said the receptionist, in a tone that said: Like, tell it to someone who cares, lady.

"This is good," I said to Ma as I guided her to a seat in the waiting room. "You're the first one here. You know, they quite often take people in the order they come in and register. You just might be the first one in to see the doctor this morning."

"I used to go to school with the doctor's mother," Ma said happily. She sat back in the chair, and a big smile lit up her face as she started to hum her favourite hymn, *The Old Rugged Cross*.

Ma and I soon found out that being first on this day at this doctor's office was definitely no bonus. Several patients had come into the office after us and had been ushered into the back. Ma was undeterred; she sat and she smiled as she hummed and she waited. *The Old Rugged Cross* was getting a good workout.

"Ma, will you be okay for a few minutes?" I asked, as the hour of ten fast approached.

"Do you have to go to work now, Bobby?" she asked.

"I'm just going to call and tell them I'll be in around noon, and I have to go feed the meter," I replied.

When I returned, Ma asked, "Did you call your office, Bobby?"

"I did. Ma, are you sure your appointment is for today?" I asked as an afterthought.

"Oh yes," Ma replied. "I called before I came down, and was told to be here this morning at eight-thirty sharp."

I approached the receptionist. "I'm sure that Mrs. Ernst must have made a mistake. Could you please verify if she has an appointment for today?" I asked.

"Yes."

"Yes, you can verify it? Or yes, she has an appointment?" I asked, and smiled as sweetly as I could. Ma may have been quite happy to be in the office of an old friend's kid, but I was getting a bit hot under the collar.

"Yes. She has an appointment," was the sarcastic response.

"Thank you," I said, and I smiled again. "You're so kind. If I can trouble you for one more thing: Would it be possible for you to tell me what time the appointment was set for?"

"The doctor will be with her shortly," she snapped.

"Oh, I was also wondering, what time does 'shortly' relate to in your little book?"

I gathered from the cold stare that I had gotten about as much information as I was going to get. Ma was still smiling and humming as I sat down beside her. She was still very pleased and quite happy to be there. We both sat and waited.

"Can you see that, Ma?" I asked Ma some time later and pointed to the large clock on the wall over the receptionist's head.

"What's that?" she asked, looking in the direction I was pointing.

"There's a clock on the wall over there, Ma, and the big hand and the little hand are both pointing straight up. It looks to me like it's high noon, pardner. I'd say it's about time to put on the old oat bag, wouldn't you?" I spoke loud enough for the receptionist—and the doctor, who was obviously lost somewhere out back—to hear. They did an admirable job of ignoring me.

"Excuse me," I said, approaching the counter, "but is it still possible for the doctor to see Mrs. Ernst before lunch?"

"The doctor has left for lunch. He'll return at two o'clock this afternoon," she said, and for the first time she smiled.

I was fit to be tied when I walked back and stared down at my grandmother's smiling face.

"You know, Ma, I don't really think this doctor cares who you went to school with. We could be here all day. Are you sure you want to stay, Ma?" I asked.

"Yes, I want to stay," she assured me. "The doctor's going to fix my eyes. I used to go to school with his mother, you know."

"Okay, Ma, but it's lunchtime. We should really go and get something to eat."

"Do you think I should go out? I don't want to miss the doctor," Ma said, and for the first time since we arrived at the doctor's office the smile disappeared from her face.

"Don't worry," I said sarcastically, "this nice friend of the family has already gone for lunch. He won't be back until two this afternoon. You can rest assured you won't miss him—you'll be back long before he is."

But Ma was enjoying her time, just sitting in that waiting room. She was at peace with the world. There was not a trace of anger, there was not even a hint of irritation.

"Listen, Ma, if you'd like to stay here, I can go out and get a sandwich for you. On the other hand, I can take you out and buy you a nice lunch. What would you like to do? Your choice, Ma. You call it."

"Well, if you think it would be okay to go out, Bobby, I would like that. But I don't want to miss the doctor," she said, and smiled again.

"Excuse me!" I called to the receptionist, "I'm just going to take my grandmother out for some lunch.

169

Would you be so kind as to save our seats for us?" I turned to Ma without waiting for a reply. "Let's go, Ma," I said. "We'll come back and see the old family friend after lunch."

When Ma attempted to stand, I was reminded of how old she had gotten. She hadn't lost any weight over the years, and sitting in a waiting room for half a day had to be very tiring on her. She did not have the same bounce in her old legs as when we had entered the office some four hours earlier. It took us a while to shuffle out to the sidewalk.

I looked around for the nearest restaurant. Just our luck, there wasn't one on our side of the street. Directly across the street there was; however, it was not just a restaurant—it was a lounge. A forbidden place.

I eyed the lounge with mixed emotions. I knew that Ma would never agree to go into a lounge, for lunch or anything else. Entering a place that served alcoholic beverages ranked with the worst of the sins. Just the thought was totally against her principles. I, too, had a problem. I was in uniform, and if there was one thing I had learned, it was never to go into a bar or lounge in uniform. I scanned the street once more, but there was nothing else available. If we were going to have lunch, it was going to be in that lounge.

We were in the middle of the block, and it didn't take a genius to realize that Ma wouldn't be able to walk to the corner, cross the street, and walk down to the lounge. There was only one thing to do: I was taking my nearly blind old grandmother across that street. We were jaywalking in the noon-hour traffic.

"C'mon, Ma," I said, taking her by the arm. "There's a real nice restaurant across the street."

We carefully stepped off the curb onto 4th Street and walked slowly between two parked cars. Two lanes of heavy traffic were going each way. I held up my hand to the oncoming traffic and stepped out ahead of Ma. Tires screeched as cars braked to a stop. Then Ma and I slowly shuffled across 4th Street. At the centre line I paused to hold up my hand for the cars going north, but Ma didn't hesitate for a second. She was moving and she was not about to stop. I waved my hand desperately, and there was more screeching of tires as alert drivers stood their cars on their noses. I breathed a sigh of relief, and waved thanks to the patient drivers when Ma and I reached the sidewalk.

Reaching the door to the lounge, I again hesitated. This was not a good idea, and I knew it; but given the circumstances, it was, I felt, the only option. I reached out and grabbed the doorknob, and arm in arm I walked through the doors with my grandmother.

Now, I had been counting on Ma's failing eyesight. With a lot of luck, she would never realize she was entering a place that served liquor. Better she should be struck dead than know she was going into such a place. After the bright sunlight, the interior of this lounge was almost as black as a moonless night. We were in luck—the lights were dim, and this lounge was one dark place. I grabbed the first table we came to and carefully guided Ma to her seat, one where she had her back to the bar and the rows of bottles displayed behind it.

171

"How's this, Ma?" I asked. "Are you comfortable?"

"I'm fine. My goodness, it sure is dark in here, isn't it?" she said as she looked around the room.

"It's like that when you come out of the sunlight and into these fancy big-city restaurants. They like to keep them dimly lit. It's more romantic," I said. "You are ready for a romantic lunch, aren't you, Ma?"

I looked at the large selection of bottles on the shelves behind the bar and prayed that she wouldn't turn her head far enough to see them.

Ma had hardly settled into her seat when a waiter appeared out of the darkness. He was a big Italian guy. The first thing I noticed was his white shirt. The top four buttons were open, framing a massive amount of hair on his chest. The buttons on his sleeves were open, and the cuffs rolled halfway to his elbows. He was one big stud.

"Can I get you something to drink?" he asked.

"Would you like something to drink, Ma?" I asked her, repeating the question. I felt it best if I took over the questioning.

"Yes, I would," she replied. "I would like a cup of hot water."

"Ma would like a cup of hot water," I said, and smiled at the waiter.

"HUH?" was his surprised comment, and his jaw dropped.

"With a shot in it," I added.

"Oh," said the waiter, and a smile of relief crossed his face.

"Make that a shot of milk—about a tablespoonful will do," I said, watching his face.

"HUH?" he said again, as if he couldn't believe what he was hearing. He looked first at Ma, then at me.

"What's the matter?" I asked. "You don't have any hot water and milk in this nice restaurant?"

"Oh, yeah . . . yeah," he answered. He stood there for several seconds in total disbelief, staring at Ma. Then without another word, he spun on his heel and almost ran away into the darkness.

"This looks like a very nice restaurant, Bobby," Ma said as she looked around the room. Her eyes never seemed to stop on any one item.

"Ma, this is one of the finest restaurants in Calgary," I assured her.

I felt sure that she couldn't see the bottles, and I felt sure that even if she had seen them, she didn't recognize them, because she had looked right at them a couple of times and her happy, contented expression never changed.

"Here's your drink, lady," said the stud, who had suddenly appeared at our table again. He set the cup and a little pitcher with milk on the table. He stayed and stared in awe as Ma took a little sip of the hot water. Then she took the pitcher and poured in a little milk, then tasted it again.

"How is it, Ma?" I asked.

"It's very good, Bobby. Thank you," she said, and smiled at the waiter. This poor guy just couldn't believe what was happening to him.

173

"Now, would you like something to eat, Ma?" I asked.

"I'd like a jam sandwich," she said. "Do you think I could have a jam sandwich?"

"Huh?" said the Italian, completely baffled by the turn his day had taken. He looked at me, and his eyes seemed to be asking: She's kidding, right?

I sat there smiling at him while he just stood with his mouth open. Then he shrugged his shoulders.

"What's the matter?" I asked him. "You maybe don't have any bread or jam?"

"Oh yeah, sure, sure. Okay," he mumbled, then turned and once more disappeared into the darkness, shaking his head.

When he returned, he did indeed have one jam sandwich on a plate. Nothing else. There was no pickle, no olive, no cherry. Just the jam sandwich. He set the plate in front of Ma without saying a word. Then he retreated to the bar, leaned his elbow on the counter, and watched Ma.

Ma picked up a half of the sandwich and took a bite.

"How is it, Ma?" I asked.

"It's very good, Bobby. It's strawberry. How did he know that strawberry was my favourite?" she asked.

"I guess that's the type of service one can expect in a good restaurant in the big city," I replied. "And our waiter is very good."

"He sure is," Ma said.

This lunch had to be the icing on the cake for Ma. It had to be the perfect day. Soon she was going to see the doctor, the child of her best friend at school. And right now she was in a beautiful restaurant, enjoying her favourite drink and her favourite jam sandwich. Yes, today the world was a beautiful place.

We sat in silence as Ma drank her hot water and ate her jam sandwich. I looked at the Italian, who was still leaning on the bar; he had not taken his eyes off Ma. I looked at my grandmother, with her favourite drink and sandwich, who was so at peace with the world — and who would have died on the spot if she had known where she was.

"Can I have the check, please?" I asked, and motioned to the waiter when Grandmother had finished eating.

"That'll be — uh . . ." he faltered. He looked around the room. Then he walked over to our table and looked down at us. He didn't know what to do, and I was sure there was nothing in the books that would tell him the price of a cup of hot water, with a shot of milk, and a strawberry jam sandwich. "There's — uh . . ." Another long pause as he glanced first at Ma and then at me. "Uh . . . oh, n-no charge," he finally blurted out.

"Are you sure?" I asked. Now it was my turn to be surprised.

"Yeah — yeah, no charge, no charge," he repeated, and again he looked at Ma and then back at me.

We walked out of the restaurant, leaving a totally bewildered waiter still standing at the bar.

Back we went, out into the blinding sunlight, onto the street. Once more I looked to the left and I held up my hand and stopped the traffic on 4th Street. Out to the centre of the street we shuffled, where I held up my right hand and stopped the other lanes of traffic. Then we walked slowly back into the doctor's office. I felt there was no need to rush. Although I had never met the child of my grandmother's school friend, I felt I already knew this doctor, only too well. I would not be coming to his clinic, at least not in this lifetime.

"Is the good doctor in this afternoon?" I asked the receptionist as we entered the waiting room.

"He'll be with you shortly," she replied icily.

At three o'clock I left the doctor's office. I fed the meter again, and then phoned my office to tell them that I would be working later tonight.

Finally, a few minutes after four in the afternoon, the receptionist took mercy on us.

"Mrs. Ernest, the doctor will see you now," she called out.

"That's Ernst," I growled at her. "She's an old family friend."

But Grandmother could have cared less. Finally she was going to see the doctor, the child of her old school friend. She had waited so patiently for more than eight hours, and she was absolutely delighted. She bounced out of the chair and strode across the floor like a spring chicken.

*   *   *

I was still fuming a few days later when my mother called.

"Bobby, did you take Ma to some fancy restaurant for lunch?" Mom's insistent question brought me back to reality.

"Yes, Mom, I did," I replied.

"Then you should be very proud of yourself!" Mom stated.

"Yeah, right," I mumbled, and wondered if I detected just a bit of sarcasm.

"Well, you should be proud," Mom said. "You know, when Ma left here, she was walking on cloud nine. All she could talk about was her old school friend and the doctor."

"Yeah, I know," I muttered. "That's all she could talk about down here too. Of course, she did sing a few lines from *The Old Rugged Cross* about a jillion times while we sat in that waiting room."

"Well, she's not talking about her old school friend and her doctor son anymore," Mom declared, and I could feel the change in her voice. "All she can talk about now is the wonderful restaurant her grandson took her to, and the nice man that brought her a cup of hot water and a strawberry jam sandwich. Where did you take her, Bobby? Have I been there?"

"I don't think so, Mom," I replied. "It was just a restaurant close to the eye doctor."

I smiled as I thought of the bottles displayed in neat rows on glass shelves in front of mirrored walls behind the bar—behind Ma. And I thought of the Italian Stud. He never did get me a drink or take my order; maybe he was afraid to ask me, for fear of what I might ask for.

177

In any event I never did get asked. But I did spend the day—the whole day—in the company of my grandmother, who, in her twilight years, couldn't have been happier.

With the world changing so rapidly, I often look back at the days I spent with my grandparents on the Stump Farm, and I'm thankful for the time I had and the lessons I learned from them. I wouldn't change those times for anything.

ROBERT J. (B0B) ADAMS

Bob Adams was born in Turner Valley, Alberta in 1938. He grew up in the Edson area, in a log house, built by his father on a farm rich in swamp spruce, tamarack, willows and muskeg.

Bob, an avid outdoorsman, was one of the fortunate few who was able to live his boyhood dreams as he entered the workforce. In 1960, after a number of years with the Alberta Forest Service and Royal Canadian Mounted Police, he began a career with the Provincial Government as a Fish and Wildlife Officer. For the next 33 years, he found his homes to include Brooks, Strathmore, Hinton, Calgary, Peace River and Edmonton.

In 1993, after a full career in Enforcement, he retired from Fish and Wildlife and wrote his first book, The Stump Farm. Today, Bob resides in Edmonton, Alberta with his wife Martha where he continues to work on his writing.

GIVE A "ROBERT J. ADAMS" BOOK TO A FRIEND

Megamy Publishing Ltd.
Box 3507
Spruce Grove, AB   T7X 3A7

Send to:
Name:_____

Street:_____

City:_____
Province/   Postal/
State:_____ Zip Code:_____

Please send:
  "The Stump Farm"   @ $16.95 = _____

  "Beyond the Stump Farm"   @ $16.95 = _____

  "Horse Cop"   @ $16.95 = _____

  "Fish Cop"   @ $16.95 = _____

  "The Elephant's Trunk"   @ $15.95 = _____

  "The South Road"   @ $16.95 = _____

  "Skunks and Hound Dogs" @ $16.95 = _____

  "In the Shadow of the Rockies" @ $16.95 = _____

  "Dynamite Hill"   @ $16.95 = _____

Shipping and handling per book   @ $ 4.00 = _____

                       7% GST = _____

Total amount enclosed: _____

Make cheque or money order payable to:
Megamy Publishing Ltd.
Price subject to change without prior notice.
ORDERS OUTSIDE OF CANADA must be paid in U.S. funds by
cheque or money order drawn on U.S. or Canadian Bank.
Sorry no C.O.D.'s.

GIVE A "ROBERT J. ADAMS" BOOK TO A FRIEND

Megamy Publishing Ltd.
Box 3507
Spruce Grove, AB   T7X 3A7

Send to:
Name:_____

Street:_____

City:_____
Province/   Postal/
State:_____ Zip Code:_____

Please send:
"The Stump Farm"   @ $16.95 =_____

"Beyond the Stump Farm"   @ $16.95 =_____

"Horse Cop"   @ $16.95 =_____

"Fish Cop"   @ $16.95 =_____

"The Elephant's Trunk"   @ $15.95 =_____

"The South Road"   @ $16.95 =_____

"Skunks and Hound Dogs"   @ $16.95 =_____

"In the Shadow of the Rockies" @ $16.95 =_____

"Dynamite Hill"   @ $16.95 =_____

Shipping and handling per book   @ $ 4.00 =_____

                                                   7% GST =_____

Total amount enclosed: _____

Make cheque or money order payable to:
Megamy Publishing Ltd.
Price subject to change without prior notice.
ORDERS OUTSIDE OF CANADA must be paid in U.S. funds by
cheque or money order drawn on U.S. or Canadian Bank.
Sorry no C.O.D.'s.